Waves and Information Technologies

elevate science
MODULES

ISBN-13: 978-1-418-29167-9   1-418-29167-6
ISBN-10:   5 20

You're an author!

As you write in this science book, your answers and personal discoveries will be recorded for you to keep, making this book unique to you. That is why you are one of the primary authors of this book.

✏️ **In the space below, print your name, school, town, and state. Then write a short autobiography that includes your interests and accomplishments.**

Your Photo

YOUR NAME ....

SCHOOL ....

TOWN, STATE ....

AUTOBIOGRAPHY ....

....

....

....

Program Authors

ZIPPORAH MILLER, EdD
Coordinator for K-12 Science Programs, Anne Arundel County Public Schools
Dr. Zipporah Miller currently serves as the Senior Manager for Organizational Learning with the Anne Arundel County Public School System. Prior to that she served as the K-12 Coordinator for science in Anne Arundel County. She conducts national training to science stakeholders on the Next Generation Science Standards. Dr. Miller also served as the Associate Executive Director for Professional Development Programs and conferences at the National Science Teachers Association (NSTA) and served as a reviewer during the development of Next Generation Science Standards. Dr. Miller holds a doctoral degree from the University of Maryland College Park, a master's degree in school administration and supervision from Bowie State University and a bachelor's degree from Chadron State College.

MICHAEL J. PADILLA, PhD
Professor Emeritus, Eugene P. Moore School of Education, Clemson University, Clemson, South Carolina
Michael J. Padilla taught science in middle and secondary schools, has more than 30 years of experience educating middle-school science teachers, and served as one of the writers of the 1996 U.S. National Science Education Standards. In recent years Mike has focused on teaching science to English Language Learners. His extensive experience as Principal Investigator on numerous National Science Foundation and U.S. Department of Education grants resulted in more than $35 million in funding to improve science education. He served as president of the National Science Teachers Association, the world's largest science teaching organization, in 2005–6.

MICHAEL E. WYSESSION, PhD
Professor of Earth and Planetary Sciences, Washington University, St. Louis, Missouri
Author of more than 100 science and science education publications, Dr. Wysession was awarded the prestigious National Science Foundation Presidential Faculty Fellowship and Packard Foundation Fellowship for his research in geophysics, primarily focused on using seismic tomography to determine the forces driving plate tectonics. Dr. Wysession is also a leader in geoscience literacy and education; he is the chair of the Earth Science Literacy Initiative, the author of several popular video lectures on geology in the *Great Courses* series, and a lead writer of the *Next Generation Science Standards**.

---

*Next Generation Science Standards is a registered trademark of Achieve. Neither Achieve nor the lead states and partners that developed the Next Generation Science Standards were involved in the production of this product, and do not endorse it. NGSS Lead States. 2013. *Next Generation Science Standards: For States, By States.* Washington, DC: The National Academies Press.

REVIEWERS

Program Consultants

Carol Baker
Science Curriculum

Dr. Carol K. Baker is superintendent for Lyons Elementary K-8 School District in Lyons, Illinois. Prior to this, she was Director of Curriculum for Science and Music in Oak Lawn, Illinois. Before this she taught Physics and Earth Science for 18 years. In the recent past, Dr. Baker also wrote assessment questions for ACT (EXPLORE and PLAN), was elected president of the Illinois Science Teachers Association from 2011–2013, and served as a member of the Museum of Science and Industry (Chicago) advisory board. She is a writer of the Next Generation Science Standards. Dr. Baker received her B.S. in Physics and a science teaching certification. She completed her master's of Educational Administration (K-12) and earned her doctorate in Educational Leadership.

Jim Cummins
ELL

Dr. Cummins's research focuses on literacy development in multilingual schools and the role technology plays in learning across the curriculum. *Elevate Science* incorporates research-based principles for integrating language with the teaching of academic content based on Dr. Cummins's work.

Elfrieda Hiebert
Literacy

Dr. Hiebert, a former primary-school teacher, is President and CEO of TextProject, a non-profit aimed at providing open-access resources for instruction of beginning and struggling readers, She is also a research associate at the University of California Santa Cruz. Her research addresses how fluency, vocabulary, and knowledge can be fostered through appropriate texts, and her contributions have been recognized through awards such as the Oscar Causey Award for Outstanding Contributions to Reading Research (Literacy Research Association, 2015), Research to Practice award (American Educational Research Association, 2013), and the William S. Gray Citation of Merit Award for Outstanding Contributions to Reading Research (International Reading Association, 2008).

Content Reviewers

Alex Blom, Ph.D.
Associate Professor
Department Of Physical Sciences
Alverno College
Milwaukee, Wisconsin

Joy Branlund, Ph.D.
Department of Physical Science
Southwestern Illinois College
Granite City, Illinois

Judy Calhoun
Associate Professor
Physical Sciences
Alverno College
Milwaukee, Wisconsin

Stefan Debbert
Associate Professor of Chemistry
Lawrence University
Appleton, Wisconsin

Diane Doser
Professor
Department of Geological Sciences
University of Texas at El Paso
El Paso, Texas

Rick Duhrkopf, Ph.D.
Department of Biology
Baylor University
Waco, Texas

Jennifer Liang
University of Minnesota Duluth
Duluth, Minnesota

Heather Mernitz, Ph.D.
Associate Professor of Physical
 Sciences
Alverno College
Milwaukee, Wisconsin

Joseph McCullough, Ph.D.
Cabrillo College
Aptos, California

Katie M. Nemeth, Ph.D.
Assistant Professor
College of Science and Engineering
University of Minnesota Duluth
Duluth, Minnesota

Maik Pertermann
Department of Geology
Western Wyoming Community College
Rock Springs, Wyoming

Scott Rochette
Department of the Earth Sciences
The College at Brockport
 State University of New York
Brockport, New York

David Schuster
Washington University in St Louis
St. Louis, Missouri

Shannon Stevenson
Department of Biology
University of Minnesota Duluth
Duluth, Minnesota

Paul Stoddard, Ph.D.
Department of Geology and
 Environmental Geosciences
Northern Illinois University
DeKalb, Illinois

Nancy Taylor
American Public University
Charles Town, West Virginia

Teacher Reviewers

Jennifer Bennett, M.A.
Memorial Middle School
Tampa, Florida

Sonia Blackstone
Lake County Schools
Howey In the Hills, Florida

Teresa Bode
Roosevelt Elementary
Tampa, Florida

Tyler C. Britt, Ed.S.
Curriculum & Instructional
  Practice Coordinator
Raytown Quality Schools
Raytown, Missouri

A. Colleen Campos
Grandview High School
Aurora, Colorado

Ronald Davis
Riverview Elementary
Riverview, Florida

Coleen Doulk
Challenger School
Spring Hill, Florida

Mary D. Dube
Burnett Middle School
Seffner, Florida

Sandra Galpin
Adams Middle School
Tampa, Florida

Margaret Henry
Lebanon Junior High School
Lebanon, Ohio

Christina Hill
Beth Shields Middle School
Ruskin, Florida

Judy Johnis
Gorden Burnett Middle School
Seffner, Florida

Karen Y. Johnson
Beth Shields Middle School
Ruskin, Florida

Jane Kemp
Lockhart Elementary School
Tampa, Florida

Denise Kuhling
Adams Middle School
Tampa, Florida

Esther Leonard, M.Ed. and L.M.T.
Gifted and talented Implementation Specialist
San Antonio Independent School District
San Antonio, Texas

Kelly Maharaj
Challenger K–8 School of Science
  and Mathematics
Spring Hill, Florida

Kevin J. Maser, Ed.D.
H. Frank Carey Jr/Sr High School
Franklin Square, New York

Angie L. Matamoros, Ph.D.
ALM Science Consultant
Weston, Florida

Corey Mayle
Brogden Middle School
Durham, North Carolina

Keith McCarthy
George Washington Middle School
Wayne, New Jersey

Yolanda O. Peña
John F. Kennedy Junior High School
West Valley City, Utah

Kathleen M. Poe
Jacksonville Beach Elementary School
Jacksonville Beach, Florida

Wendy Rauld
Monroe Middle School
Tampa, Florida

Anne Rice
Woodland Middle School
Gurnee, Illinois

Bryna Selig
Gaithersburg Middle School
Gaithersburg, Maryland

Pat (Patricia) Shane, Ph.D.
STEM & ELA Education Consultant
Chapel Hill, North Carolina

Diana Shelton
Burnett Middle School
Seffner, Florida

Nakia Sturrup
Jennings Middle School
Seffner, Florida

Melissa Triebwasser
Walden Lake Elementary
Plant City, Florida

Michele Bubley Wiehagen
Science Coach
Miles Elementary School
Tampa, Florida

Pauline Wilcox
Instructional Science Coach
Fox Chapel Middle School
Spring Hill, Florida

Safety Reviewers

Douglas Mandt, M.S.
Science Education Consultant
Edgewood, Washington

Juliana Textley, Ph.D.
Author, NSTA books on school science safety
Adjunct Professor
Lesley University
Cambridge, Massachusetts

Waves and Electromagnetic Radiation x

Go to PearsonRealize.com
to access your digital course.

▶ **VIDEO**
- Lighting Designer

🔵 **INTERACTIVITY**
- Modeling Waves
- Making Waves
- Describe the Properties of Waves
- Model Wave Interactions
- Use Models to Describe Wave Behavior
- Reflection, Transmission, and Absorption of Sound Waves
- Sound
- Doppler Effect
- Build an Electromagnetic Wave
- Models of Light
- Describe Electromagnetic Waves
- Describe the Behavior of Light
- Blinded by the Light
- Predict the Behavior of Light Rays

📱 **VIRTUAL LAB**
- Color of the Sky

☑ **ASSESSMENT**

📖 **eTEXT**

HANDS-ON LABS

Connect What Are Waves?

Investigate
- Waves and Their Characteristics
- Standing Waves and Wave Interference
- Understanding Sound
- Build a Wave
- Light Interacting with Matter

Demonstrate
Making Waves

Information Technologies 62

Why are digital signals a reliable way to produce, store, and transmit information?

Quest KICKOFF Testing, Testing . . . 1, 2, 3 64

иConnect Lab Continuous or Discrete? 65A

MS-PS4-3

Go to PearsonRealize.com to access your digital course.

▶ **VIDEO**
- Network Administrator

👆 **INTERACTIVITY**
- Electric Circuits
- How Can You Light the Lights?
- Analog and Digital Signals
- I've Got to Take This Call
- Digitized Images
- Film Cameras and Digital Cameras
- Technology and Communication
- Signal Reliability

💻 **VIRTUAL LAB**
- Super Spy!

☑ **ASSESSMENT**

📖 **eTEXT**

HANDS-ON LABS

иConnect Continuous or Discrete?

иInvestigate
- Electric Current and Voltage
- Constructing a Simple Computer Circuit
- Let the Music Play

иDemonstrate
Over and Out

Elevate Teaching!

Teaching science has never been more important. *Elevate Science* helps you transform learning, promote innovation, and manage your classroom. It elevates teaching to a new level with student-centered activities based on new science standards. Realistic goals, best practices, and simple explanations make teaching practical and rewarding. Share the wonder and promote curiosity and inventiveness.

This is *Elevate Science*.

Transform

Transform your science classroom by immersing students in active, three-dimensional learning. *Elevate Science* engages students with real-world tasks, open-ended investigations, and in the engineering/design process.

- A new **3-D learning model** enhances best practices.

- **Engineering-focused** features infuse STEM learning.

- **Phenomena-based** activities put students at the heart of a Quest for knowledge.

DESIGN CHALLENGE Can you put your own decomposers to work and build your own composter? Go to the Engineering Design Notebook to find out!

uDemonstrate Lab

Changes in an Ecosystem

How does a **forest fire** disrupt a long-leaf pine forest and **affect populations of organisms**?

Background

Forest fires have a bad reputation! Indeed, many forest fires can endanger habitats, human life, and property. But, forest fires can also serve an important function by changing the physical and biological components in a longleaf pine ecosystem. How does a forest fire disrupt a longleaf pine forest and affect populations of organisms?

Quest KICKOFF

How can you use solids, liquids, and gases to lift a car?

STEM Phenomenon Auto mechanics often need to go under cars to repair the parts in the under-carriage, such as the shocks and exhaust system. It's much easier for them to do their job if they have more room to work, so they use lift systems to raise the cars overhead. In this problem-based Quest activity, you will design an elevator or lift system that uses a solid, liquid, or gas to raise a model car. You will explore the properties of solids, liquids, and gases to see how they can be used in a lift mechanism. You will investigate how potential changes of state affect

Innovate

Focus on 21st century skills. Encourage students to think, collaborate, and innovate! With *Elevate Science*, your students will explore STEM careers, experience engineering activities, and discover our scientific and technological world.

- **Problem-based learning** Quests put students on a journey of discovery.

- **STEM connections** help integrate curriculum.

- **Coding and innovation** engage students and build **21st century skills**.

CAREERS
Energy Engineer
Reinventing ENERGY SYSTEMS

MS-PS3-5

Quest CHECK-IN

IN LESSON 3

STEM What criteria and constraints affect your model? Build and test your lift device. Improve and retest as needed.

HANDS-ON LAB

Phases of Matter

Manage

Feel confident teaching science. The content, strategies, and resources of *Elevate Science* equip your classroom for scientific inquiry and science and engineering practices. You'll lead your class in asking questions and engaging in argumentation.

- **Evidence-based assessments** provide new options for monitoring student understanding.

- **Professional development** offers practical point-of-use support.

- **Embedded standards** in the program allow for integration.

- **ELL and differentiated instruction** strategies help instructors reach every learner.

- **Interdisciplinary connections** relate science to other subjects.

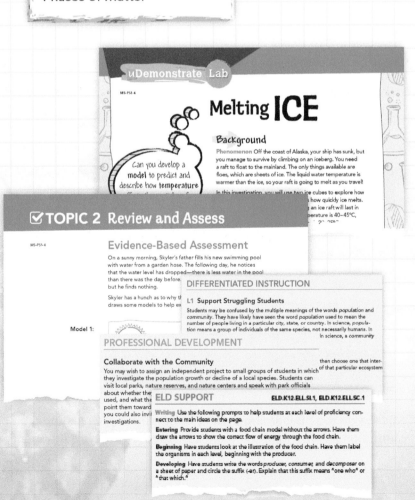

uDemonstrate Lab

MS-PS1-4

Melting ICE

Can you develop a model to predict and describe how temperature

Background
Phenomenon Off the coast of Alaska, your ship has sunk, but you manage to survive by climbing on an iceberg. You need a raft to float to the mainland. The only things available are floes, which are sheets of ice. The liquid water temperature is warmer than the ice, so your raft is going to melt as you travel!

In this investigation, you will use two ice cubes to explore how quickly ice melts. an ice raft will last in perature is 40–45°C,

☑ TOPIC 2 Review and Assess

MS-PS1-4

Evidence-Based Assessment

On a sunny morning, Skyler's father fills his new swimming pool with water from a garden hose. The following day, he notices that the water level has dropped—there is less water in the pool than there was the day before. but he finds nothing.

Skyler has a hunch as to why draws some models to help ex

Model 1:

DIFFERENTIATED INSTRUCTION

L1 Support Struggling Students
Students may be confused by the multiple meanings of the words *population* and *community*. They have likely have seen the word *population* used to mean the number of people living in a particular city, state, or country. In science, *population* means a group of individuals of the same species, not necessarily humans. In science, a *community*

PROFESSIONAL DEVELOPMENT

Collaborate with the Community
You may wish to assign an independent project to small groups of students in which they investigate the population growth or decline of a local species. Students can visit local parks, nature reserves, and nature centers and speak with park officials about whether the used, and what the point them towar you could also invi investigations.

then choose one that inter-of that particular ecosystem

ELD SUPPORT   ELD.K12.ELL.SI.1, ELD.K12.ELL.SC.1

Writing Use the following prompts to help students at each level of proficiency connect to the main ideas on the page.

Entering Provide students with a food chain model without the arrows. Have them draw the arrows to show the correct flow of energy through the food chain.

Beginning Have students look at the illustration of the food chain. Have them label the organisms in each level, beginning with the producer.

Developing Have students write the words *producer, consumer,* and *decomposer* on a sheet of paper and circle the suffix (-er). Explain that this suffix means "one who" or "that which."

Elevate Learning!

NEXT GENERATION INSTRUCTIONAL MODEL

New standards call for a new way to learn. *Elevate Science* empowers students to become more self-directed, curious, and accountable. Students learn to synthesize ideas, use evidence, and demonstrate their understandings of key concepts and skills.

> *"One-dimensional thinking is to 'know something'. Three-dimensional thinking is to know something and be able to apply it in context under conditions that reflect real life."*
>
> – DR. WILLIAM SPADY
> Seeds of Tomorrow

CONNECT	INVESTIGATE	SYNTHESIZE	DEMONSTRATE
ENGAGE the mind with phenomena, linking what students know to their own personal experiences.	**EXPLORE** concepts and ideas while constructing knowledge and building meaning.	**EXPLAIN** and **ELABORATE** understanding by formulating ideas, arguments, and solutions using evidence.	**ELABORATE** and **EVALUATE** arguments by applying newly formed understandings and transferring knowledge to new situations.
ENGAGE	EXPLORE	EXPLAIN ELABORATE	EVALUATE

Based on the 5E learning cycle, this new instructional model blends print and digital learning into a seamless student-centered experience.

REALIZE A BETTER WAY!

New — Realize Reader!

- On-the-go access for mobile devices

- Offline access with auto sync when internet is available

- Intuitive tools for quick search, annotations, highlighting

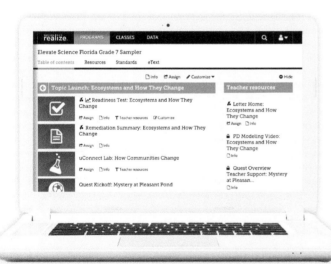

Customize Curriculum

- Re-order topic and lesson resources

- Edit program resources and assessments

- Upload your own content

Powerful Partners

- Access content from Google Expeditions

- Compatible with Google© Classrooms and Open Ed

- Embedded littleBits™ engineering activities

SCOPE AND SEQUENCE

Waves and Information Technology

TOPIC 1 Waves and Electromagnetic Radiation

 What are the properties of mechanical and electromagnetic waves?

Quest Design to Stop a Thief

TOPIC 2 Information Technologies

 Why are digital signals a reliable way to produce, store, and transmit information?

Quest Testing, Testing...1, 2, 3

Essential Questions
Each topic begins with an Essential Question that will introduce, drive, and frame student learning. Revisit the Essential Questions with your students as they master the component ideas and practices within the topics.

A Quest in Every Topic
Quests are problem-based learning projects for students to complete as they progress through the topics. Each multipart project brings the topic content to life by providing an opportunity for students take on a real-world problem. Quest activities also reinforce connecting concepts, communication and collaboration skills, and understanding of the nature and processes of science.

Next Generation Science Standards Correlation

Waves and Information Technology
Students who demonstrate understanding can:

Performance Expectation MS-PS4-1	Where to find it
Use mathematical representations to describe a simple model for waves that includes how the amplitude of a wave is related to the energy in a wave.	**SE** pp. 1–3, 4–11, 54–57 **TE** pp. 1–3, 4–11, 54–57
DISCIPLINARY CORE IDEA	
PS4.A: Wave Properties A simple wave has a repeating pattern with a specific wavelength, frequency, and amplitude.	**SE** pp. 4–11, 24–33 **TE** pp. 4–11, 24–33
SCIENCE AND ENGINEERING PRACTICE	
Using Mathematics and Computational Thinking Use mathematical representations to describe and/or support scientific conclusions and design solutions. **Connection to Nature of Science** Science knowledge is based upon logical and conceptual connections between evidence and explanations.	**SE** pp. 4–11, 86–87 **TE** pp. 4–11, 86–87
CROSSCUTTING CONCEPT	
Patterns Graphs and charts can be used to identify patterns in data.	**SE** pp. 4–11, 91, 100–101 **TE** pp. 4–11, 91, 100–101

Performance Expectation MS-PS4-2	Where to find it
Develop and use a model to describe that waves are reflected, absorbed, or transmitted through various materials.	**SE** pp. 16, 20, 27, 33, 36-37, 48–52, 58–61
	TE pp. 16, 20, 27, 33, 36-37, 48–52, 58–61

DISCIPLINARY CORE IDEA

PS4.B: Electromagnetic Radiation • When light shines on an object, it is reflected, absorbed, or transmitted through the object, depending on the object's material and the frequency (color) of the light. • The path that light travels can be traced as straight lines, except at surfaces between different transparent materials (e.g., air and water, air and glass) where the light path bends. • A wave model of light is useful for explaining brightness, color, and the frequency-dependent bending of light at a surface between media. • However, because light can travel through space, it cannot be a matter wave, like sound or water waves.	**SE** pp.14–22, 25–28, 33, 34–42, 44–53, 56–57 **TE** pp. 14–22, 25–28, 33, 34–42, 44–53, 56–57

SCIENCE AND ENGINEERING PRACTICE

Developing and Using Models Develop and use a model to describe phenomena.	**SE** pp. 14–22, 24–33, 34–42, 44–53, 94 **TE** pp. 14–22, 24–33, 34–42, 44–53, 94

CROSSCUTTING CONCEPT

Structure and Function Structures can be designed to serve particular functions by taking into account properties of different materials, and how materials can be shaped and used.	**SE** pp. 14–22, 24–33, 34–42, 44–53 **TE** pp. 14–22, 24–33, 34–42, 44–53

Next Generation Science Standards Correlation

Performance Expectation MS-PS4-3	Where to find it
Integrate qualitative scientific and technical information to support the claim that digitized signals are a more reliable way to encode and transmit information than analog signals.	**SE** pp. pp. 62–65, 66–74, 76–85, 86–87, 88–96, 98–101, 102–105
	TE pp. 62–65, 66–74, 76–85, 86–87, 88–96, 98–101, 102–105
DISCIPLINARY CORE IDEA	
PS4.C: Information Technologies and Instrumentation Digitized signals (sent as wave pulses) are a more reliable way to encode and transmit information.	**SE** pp. 62–65, 66–74, 76–85, 86–87, 88–96, 98–101, 102–105
	TE pp. 62–65, 66–74, 76–85, 86–87, 88–96, 98–101, 102–105
SCIENCE AND ENGINEERING PRACTICE	
Obtaining, Evaluating, and Communicating Information Integrate qualitative scientific and technical information in written text with that contained in media and visual displays to clarify claims and findings.	**SE** pp. 62–65, 66–74, 76–85, 86–87, 88–96, 98–101, 102–105
	TE pp. 62–65, 66–74, 76–85, 86–87, 88–96, 98–101, 102–105
CROSSCUTTING CONCEPT	
Structure and Function Structures can be designed to serve particular functions. **Connections to Engineering, Technology, and Applications of Science** Technologies extend the measurement, exploration, modeling, and computational capacity of scientific investigations. **Connections to Nature of Science** Advances in technology influence the progress of science and science has influenced advances in technology.	**SE** pp. 62–65, 66–74, 76–85, 86–87, 88–96, 98–101, 102–105
	TE pp. 62–65, 66–74, 76–85, 86–87, 88–96, 98–101, 102–105

PACING GUIDE

The guide on these pages suggests the amount of time to spend on each lesson of each topic in the Elevate Science book. Time allotments include lab activities and assessments.

Waves and Information Technology

Days (approx.)

TOPIC 1 Waves and Electromagnetic Radiation

Topic Opener.. 1 day

Lesson 1 Wave Properties... 3 days

Lesson 2 Wave Interactions .... 4 days

Lesson 3 Sound Waves .... 3 days

Lesson 4 Electromagnetic Waves .... 3 days

Lesson 5 Electromagnetic Radiation .... 3 days

Lab: uDemonstrate .... 2 days

Assessment .... 1 day

TOPIC 2 Information Technologies

Topic Opener.. 1 day

Lesson 1 Electric Circuits .... 4 days

Lesson 2 Signals.. 3 days

Lesson 3 Communication and Technology .... 3 days

Lab: uDemonstrate .... 2 days

Assessment .... 1 day

School to Home Letter

Dear Family Member,

As your child's science teacher, I am looking forward to helping your child learn about science. Because I know that you want your child to be successful, I offer these suggestions so that you can help your child gain proficiency in science.

- Your child's textbook is very different from most—it's meant for students to write in it. Therefore, it is a record of learning. Look through lessons your child has completed recently, and be sure to ask lots of questions. One of the best ways for students to check on their learning is to explain it to someone else.
- Ask your child about homework assignments and check that he or she has completed them.
- Help your child collect materials and information for school activities.
- Encourage computer literacy. Advise your child to use computers in school or at the library. If you have a home computer, help your child do research online.

Throughout this program, your child will be introduced to waves, electromagnetic radiation and information technologies.

I encourage you to stay involved in your child's learning. By all means, visit the classroom during open house or make an appointment with me if you have questions.

Cordially,

Science Teacher

Waves and Electromagnetic Radiation

STORYLINE	SELECT TOPIC RESOURCES	
TOPIC LAUNCH		
Each day, students encounter many forms of energy transmission through waves. Students explore and examine the different properties of these waves and the way that the waves interact with matter and with each other. Through this study, they also learn the ways in which electromagnetic waves are particularly relevant to our lives and to the technologies that we use every day.	▶ **VIDEO** Professional Development .... (5) ☑ **ASSESSMENT** Topic Readiness Test .... (15) 📄 **DOCUMENT** L1 Topic Remediation Summary ...... (15)	🧪 **иConnect Lab** .... (15) **Essential Question** .... (5) 👆 **INTERACTIVITY** *Quest* KICKOFF (10)
LESSON 1 Wave Properties		
Students examine and model different properties of waves. They compare the properties of different types of waves and compare how different types of waves transfer energy.	🧪 **иInvestigate Lab** .... (60) 👆 **INTERACTIVITY** *Quest* CHECK-IN (10) Case Study .... (15)	📄 **DOCUMENTS** L1 Remediation .... (15) L3 Enrichment .... (15)
LESSON 2 Wave Interactions		
Students investigate the ways that waves can react when they strike materials and the effects of interactions between waves.	🧪 **иInvestigate Lab** .... (25) 👆 **INTERACTIVITY** *Quest* CHECK-IN (20) ▶ **VIDEO** Engineering Video .... (5)	**Engineering Design Notebook** .... (20) 📄 **DOCUMENTS** L1 Remediation .... (15) L3 Enrichment .... (15)

NEXT GENERATION SCIENCE STANDARDS

MS-PS4-1 Use mathematical representations to describe a simple model for waves that includes how the amplitude of a wave is related to the energy in a wave.

MS-PS4-2 Develop and use a model to describe that waves are reflected, absorbed, or transmitted through various materials.

STORYLINE	SELECT TOPIC RESOURCES

LESSON 3 Sound Waves

Students investigate how sound waves interact with matter through reflection, absorption, transmittal, and diffraction and how properties of materials affect the speed of sound.

🧪 *u*Investigate Lab .... (30)

📄 DOCUMENTS

L1 Remediation .... (15)

L3 Enrichment .... (15)

LESSON 4 Electromagnetic Waves

Students learn about the different types of electromagnetic waves, how they compare, and how they are used.

🧪 *u*Investigate Lab .... (40)

Career Feature .... (20)

▶ VIDEO
Career Video .... (15)

👆 INTERACTIVITY *Quest* CHECK-IN .... (30)

📄 DOCUMENTS

L1 Remediation .... (15)

L3 Enrichment .... (15)

LESSON 5 Light

Students model light-matter interactions to determine how transparent, translucent, opaque, and colored materials reflect and absorb light. Students also model how light interacts with concave and convex lenses.

🧪 *u*Investigate Lab .... (55)

🧪 HANDS-ON LAB *Quest* CHECK-IN .... (45)

🧪 Virtual Lab .... (20)

📄 DOCUMENTS

L1 Remediation .... (15)

L3 Enrichment .... (15)

TOPIC CLOSE

As students apply their knowledge of different wave types to their understanding of energy and matter, they learn how different wave characteristics and behaviors are important to Earth's systems.

TOPIC 1 Review and Assess .... (30)

☑ ASSESSMENT
Topic Test .... (40)

👆 INTERACTIVITY

L1 Topic Remediation .... (10)

👆 INTERACTIVITY *Quest* FINDINGS .... (40)

🧪 *u*Demonstrate Lab .... (40)

SHORT ON TIME?
◯ Use these assets with the yellow clock.

DIFFERENTIATED INSTRUCTION
L1 Struggling Students   L3 Advanced Students

Waves and Electromagnetic Radiation

Use the grade-band endpoints identified below to help you prioritize instruction and integrate the dimensions.
MS-PS4-1, MS-PS4-2

	Grades 3–5 Students should already be capable of . . .	**Grades 6–8** Students are working toward . . .
SCIENCE AND ENGINEERING PRACTICES		developing and/or revising models to show the relationships among variables.
SEP.2 Developing and Using Models	developing and using models to describe and/or predict phenomena.	using mathematical representations to describe or support scientific conclusions.
SEP.5 Using Mathematics and Computational Thinking	describing and measuring quantities to address scientific questions and problems.	
		recognizing that a simple wave has a repeating pattern with a specific wavelength, frequency, and amplitude.
DISCIPLINARY CORE IDEAS		
PS4.A Wave Properties	understanding that waves are regular patterns of motion.	realizing that light striking an object is reflected, absorbed, or transmitted.
PS4.B Electromagnetic Radiation	understanding that an object can be seen when light striking its surface enters the eye.	
		using graphs and charts to identify patterns in data.
CROSSCUTTING CONCEPTS		
CCC.1 Patterns	developing a model of waves showing amplitude and wavelength.	recognizing that the properties of a material influence how that material can be shaped and used.
CCC.6 Structure and Function	understanding that different materials have different substructures.	

Grades 9–12
Students will develop the skills of . . .

developing and/or revising models based on evidence to show relationships between systems.

using mathematical, computational, or algorithmic representations to describe and support claims or explanations.

understanding that wavelength and frequency are related to one another by a wave's speed of travel.

recognizing that electromagnetic radiation can be modeled as changing electric and magnetic fields or as photons.

analyzing and interpreting patterns to improve the design of a system.

examining the properties of different materials when investigating systems or structures.

College & Careers
As adults, students can apply these skills by . . .

evaluating and using technology systems to maximize sound quality.

using knowledge of wavelength and frequency to record, edit, and mix sound.

pursuing a career as a sound engineer, helping to shape the artistic and technical elements of music.

Waves and Electromagnetic Radiation

Using Phenomena Students observe the phenomena of water waves and light waves and explain how they think these two different types of waves are similar.

HANDS-ON LAB

📄 **GO ONLINE to download...**

иConnect

Students will explore how the shape of a wave changes as energy moves through it. They will also observe how the different parts of a wave change shape.

Class Time (15)

Group Size groups

Materials (per group) 5-meter section of rope or clothesline, white or fluorescent tape

Procedure Tips
Remind students to keep a tight hold on the rope to avoid injury or damage to items in the classroom. Have each student make their own observations about the movement of the tape, paying close attention to where the tape is in relation to their arm position as they make a wave.

NEXT GENERATION SCIENCE STANDARDS

MS-PS4-1 Use mathematical representations to describe a simple model for waves that includes how the amplitude of a wave is related to the energy in a wave.

MS-PS4-2 Develop and use a model to describe that waves are reflected, absorbed, or transmitted through various materials.

Waves and Electromagnetic Radiation

Waves and Electromagnetic Radiation

NGSS PERFORMANCE EXPECTATIONS

MS-PS4-1 Use mathematical representations to describe a simple model for waves that includes how the amplitude of a wave is related to the energy in a wave.
MS-PS4-2 Develop and use a model to describe that waves are reflected, absorbed, or transmitted through various materials.

HANDS-ON LAB

иConnect See how particles on a wave move in this rope experiment.

Topic Materials List

📄 **GO ONLINE to download a detailed, editable master materials list.**

Consumables
- white or fluorescent tape
- paper towels
- narrow tape or ribbon
- paper cups
- craft sticks
- glue
- cotton string

Nonconsumables
- rope or clothesline
- plastic droppers
- metric rulers
- modeling clay
- plastic knives
- corks or other small floating objects
- ripple tanks
- spring toys
- shallow pans

- small stones
- rope
- meter sticks
- stopwatches
- tennis balls
- protractors
- buckets
- wooden boards with guitar strings
- sharpened pencils or scissors
- long water pipes

- small hammers or rulers
- cotton string
- general materials for models (e.g., wire, cardboard, dryer hose, pipe insulators, dry macaroni, toothpicks, wood)

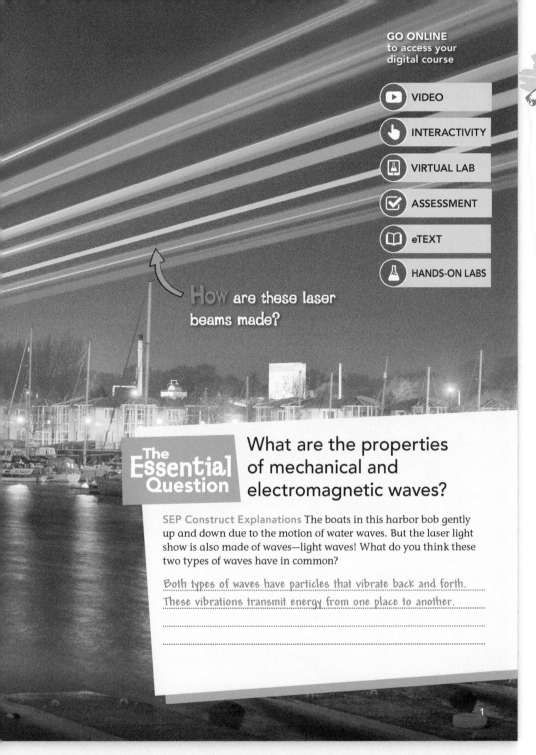

GO ONLINE
to access your
digital course

- ▶ VIDEO
- 👆 INTERACTIVITY
- 🔬 VIRTUAL LAB
- ☑ ASSESSMENT
- 📖 eTEXT
- ⚗ HANDS-ON LABS

How are these laser beams made?

The Essential Question

What are the properties of mechanical and electromagnetic waves?

SEP Construct Explanations The boats in this harbor bob gently up and down due to the motion of water waves. But the laser light show is also made of waves—light waves! What do you think these two types of waves have in common?

Both types of waves have particles that vibrate back and forth.
These vibrations transmit energy from one place to another.
‒‒‒
‒‒‒

 1

DIFFERENTIATED INSTRUCTION

L1 Support Struggling Students
Help students relate the word *wave* to motion and thus to energy. Ask students what they think of when they hear the word *wave*. Point out that most uses of the term describe a motion. This makes sense, because waves are a transfer of energy and the transfer of energy involves motion.

L3 Support Advanced Students
Ask students what they think of when they hear the word *wave*. Point out that, in science, a wave is a transfer of energy. Ask, *Which of the waves you listed describes a transfer of energy?* Encourage discussion. For this exercise, the emphasis is on students supporting their arguments using evidence based on observations.

🔍 Focus on Mastery!

Using Phenomena Have students inspect the photo of the laser show. Have them work with a partner to predict what the laser beams are made of. Ask them to think about times that they've heard about or seen laser beams in movies, television shows, or even their daily life. What kinds of things are lasers used for? Why do you think lasers are used instead of regular light beams for laser shows? As a group, share students' predictions and have students write down one question that they might have about the photo.

Discuss with the class: **How are these laser beams made?**

The Essential Question

Activate Prior Knowledge
SEP Construct Explanations As a warm-up activity, ask students to…

- describe to a partner what happens when a wave moves across the surface of a body of water.
- discuss in small groups how energy, such as that in a water wave, can move through matter. Have students draw diagrams to illustrate their explanations and descriptions of energy movement.
- share some examples of energy movement with the class.

Read the Essential Question to the class. Ask: How might waves differ, and what are some different types of energy that might move in waves?

Assessment and Remediation

☑ ASSESSMENT

GO ONLINE to access…
Topic Readiness Test Use the auto-graded online assessment to determine whether your students are prepared for success in the upcoming topic. **Editable**

📄 DOCUMENT

GO ONLINE to download…
L1 Remediation Summary Support struggling students by providing additional preparation before beginning the topic **Editable**.

Quest KICKOFF

▶ **VIDEO**

GO ONLINE to access...
Design to Stop a Thief Students watch a 5-minute video and respond to question prompts to get them thinking about what lasers are and how they are used.

STEM **Connect to the Real World: Everyday Laser Technology** Have students discuss in small groups the ways that their daily lives involve the use of lasers.

- Ask students to write out a list of items that they use every day involving lasers. Some students might provide the same answers; in this case, have students mark that more than one student uses that technology.
- As a class, discuss some ways that these technologies could be improved. For example, students could discuss how the lasers in grocery store scanners could be improved to work better on bar codes that are difficult to scan, such bar codes on glossy or curved surfaces.
- Finally, have students create an exit ticket with one question about a specific laser technology that they have encountered during the discussion. Have students present their ticket before leaving the classroom for the day.

NEXT GENERATION SCIENCE STANDARDS

MS-PS4-1 Use mathematical representations to describe a simple model for waves that includes how the amplitude of a wave is related to the energy in a wave.

MS-PS4-2 Develop and use a model to describe that waves are reflected, absorbed, or transmitted through various materials.

Quest KICKOFF

How can you design a system to stop a thief?

■ **NBC LEARN** ▶ **VIDEO**

STEM **Phenomenon** It may seem like something out of the movies, but some security systems use lasers to help prevent the theft of priceless objects. Engineers apply their knowledge of light and how it behaves to design these security systems. In this Quest activity, you will explore how light waves interact with lenses and mirrors. You will design possible solutions for a security demonstration and then test and evaluate your solutions to determine the optimal design. After making any additional modifications, you will demonstrate your expertise by directing a beam of light around an obstacle to reach

After watching the Quest Kickoff video, think about a problem in your community that might be solved with the use of lasers. Record your solutions. Then share your ideas with a partner and discuss how lasers are important to our daily lives.

Sample: A raccoon can make a huge mess as it raids a trash bin in search of food. Lasers can be used to detect a raccoon approaching a trash bin, then trigger a bright light to scare the raccoon away.

👆 **INTERACTIVITY**

Design to Stop a Thief

MS-PS4-1 Use mathematical representations to describe a simple model for waves that includes how the amplitude of a wave is related to the energy in a wave.
MS-PS4-2 Develop and use a model to describe that waves are reflected, absorbed, or transmitted through various materials.

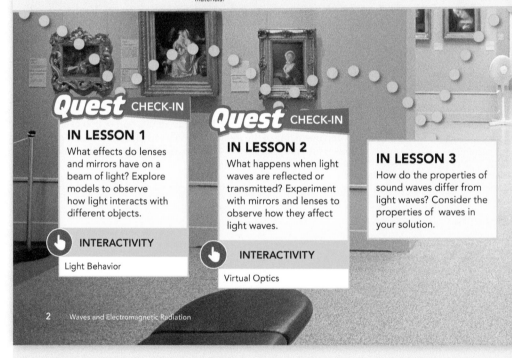

Quest CHECK-IN

IN LESSON 1
What effects do lenses and mirrors have on a beam of light? Explore models to observe how light interacts with different objects.

👆 **INTERACTIVITY**

Light Behavior

Quest CHECK-IN

IN LESSON 2
What happens when light waves are reflected or transmitted? Experiment with mirrors and lenses to observe how they affect light waves.

👆 **INTERACTIVITY**

Virtual Optics

IN LESSON 3
How do the properties of sound waves differ from light waves? Consider the properties of waves in your solution.

PROFESSIONAL DEVELOPMENT

Content Refresher

As you work through the lesson with students, reinforce the idea that the energy used by most plants and animals to live originally came from from the sun in the form of electromagnetic waves. Ultraviolet light (UV light) from the sun is used by photosynthetic organisms to make stored energy in food. UV light is also used by the human body to make its own vitamin D. Furthermore, UV light and energy from the rest of the electromagnetic spectrum can be harnessed by solar energy technology for use with electronic devices.

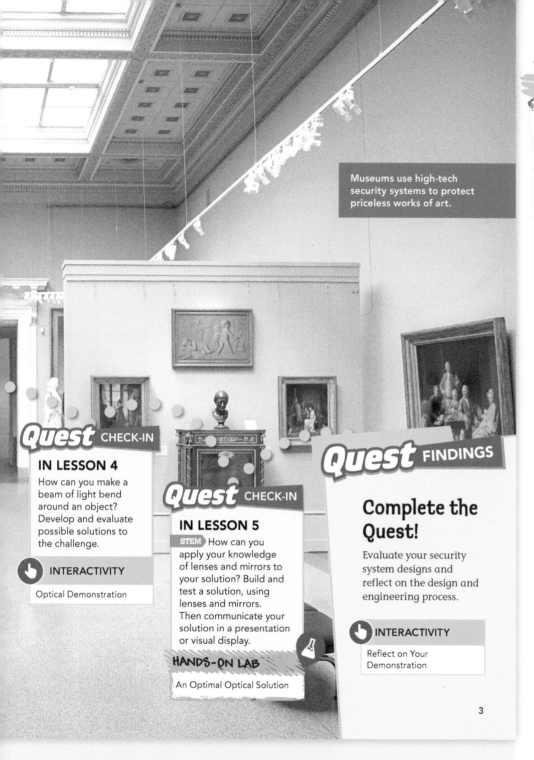

Museums use high-tech security systems to protect priceless works of art.

Anchoring Phenomenon In this Quest activity, students analyze a problem and design an effective laser security system that can stop a thief. Before beginning the development of a design, students should understand the problem as much as possible by asking questions and gathering information. Guide students in understanding the importance of the following parts of the design process:

- identifying the problem
- determining who or what is affected by the problem
- choosing what to change to solve the problem

Encourage students to apply their answers to the Quest activity as they work through each stage. Remind them that they can test and revise their security system models to provide the most effective protection.

Quest CHECK-IN

IN LESSON 4
How can you make a beam of light bend around an object? Develop and evaluate possible solutions to the challenge.

👆 **INTERACTIVITY**

Optical Demonstration

Quest CHECK-IN

IN LESSON 5
STEM How can you apply your knowledge of lenses and mirrors to your solution? Build and test a solution, using lenses and mirrors. Then communicate your solution in a presentation or visual display.

HANDS-ON LAB

An Optimal Optical Solution

Quest FINDINGS

Complete the Quest!

Evaluate your security system designs and reflect on the design and engineering process.

👆 **INTERACTIVITY**

Reflect on Your Demonstration

3

📄 DOCUMENT

GO ONLINE to download...
Quest Checklist Students monitor their own progress as they complete the steps leading up to the Quest Findings. **Editable**

📄 DOCUMENT

GO ONLINE to download...
Quest Rubric Assess students on their ability to ask questions, define problems, create and revise solutions, and draw conclusions. Encourage peer review and self-reflection as students use the grading rubric to review a draft of their Findings before turning in their final versions. **Editable**

DIFFERENTIATED INSTRUCTION

L1 Support Struggling Students
Provide students with a graphic organizer that they can use to collect the information for their Findings as they work through each Check-In.

L3 Support Advanced Students
Have students research the development of one type of laser technology from its discovery to its state today. Direct them to include examples of the technology's current use.

TOPIC 1

uConnect Lab

Investigative Phenomenon Some kinds of waves can be difficult to observe, so making a model is a good way for students to begin to understand waves. Ask students to think about different things that are described as waves, such as ocean waves or wavy hair, and what those things have in common.

Purpose

Students will use a model to explore how the shape of a wave changes as energy moves through it. They will also observe how the different parts of a wave change shape.

Class Time (25)

Group Size Groups

📄 **GO ONLINE to download...**
the master materials list, which also identifies kit materials.

Safety

Students should wear their safety goggles throughout this activity. Instruct students not to yank on the ropes so hard that they pull it from their partner's hands. The ropes should not be used for anything other than this activity.

Advance Preparation (15 minutes)

Cut the lengths of rope ahead of time. To save in-class time, you might want to put the tape on the ropes before class as well.

uConnect Lab

What Are Waves?

Background

Phenomenon You've seen waves before, but do you know what waves really are? In this activity, you will observe waves and draw a conclusion about what waves are.

How can you **use a model** to understand waves?

Materials

(per group)
- 5-meter length of rope or clothesline
- colored tape

Safety

Be sure to follow all safety procedures provided by your teacher. The Safety Appendix of your textbook provides more details about the safety icons.

Design a Procedure

☐ 1. 🧪 Wrap a piece of tape around the rope at approximately the halfway point.

☐ 2. You will send waves along the rope. Predict how the waves will change the position of the piece of tape.
   Sample: The tape will move up and down.

☐ 3. SEP Plan an Investigation Write a procedure that uses the rope and tape to model waves.
   _____
   _____
   _____
   _____
   _____
   _____
   _____
   _____

☐ 4. Show your plan to your teacher before you begin. Then, use your materials to model a wave. Draw a sketch of your model and describe it.

SAMPLE PROCEDURE

If your students need more direction on this lab, use the following procedure to guide their work.

1. 🧪 Wrap a 10-cm length of tape around the rope at approximately the halfway point.

2. Hold one end of the rope while your partner holds the other end. Face your partner and move away from each other until the rope is extended to nearly its full length. Don't pull the rope tight. Move your end of the rope about half a meter up and down once quickly to send a single wave along the rope. Observe the rope and tape.

3. When the wave reaches the other end of the rope, have your partner send a wave back toward you. Again, observe the rope and tape.

Sketch

HANDS-ON LAB

Connect Go online for a downloadable worksheet of this lab.

Analyze and Interpret Data

1. **Explain Phenomena** What happened to the rope and tape? Was your prediction correct?

   Sample: As the wave travelled down the rope, The piece of tape travelled up and down. This matched my prediction.

2. **SEP Construct an Explanation** Without using the word "wave," describe what you think moved from one end of the rope to the other end.

   Energy travelled up and down the length of the rope.

3B

Focus on Mastery!

SEP Use Models Students will use models to understand that waves transfer energy from place to place. Waves travel through matter and they are not tangible, though they can be observed. They often cause physical changes to matter, such as the ocean ebbing and flowing. Objects on or in the matter can change position as a result of waves, like a boat bobbing up and down in the water. In small groups, have students discuss the following: What did the rope represent? Why did you have to use a model to show how waves move?

HANDS-ON LAB

📄 **GO ONLINE to download...**

this lab and additional teacher support. **Editable**

Procedure Tips

- **Step 2** You might have to demonstrate how to move the rope to make a large enough wave to observe.

Expected Outcomes

- Students will use models to observe waves and draw a conclusion about what waves are. Students will observe that the wave travelled up and down the rope and begin to understand that energy moves in waves.

NOTES

Wave Properties

OBJECTIVES

Students will evaluate evidence and claims that

- different types of waves transmit energy in different ways.
- waves share common properties that influence the waves' behavior.

Students will analyze cause-and-effect relationships and determine how

- frequency, wavelength, and speed are related.

Students will use patterns described in a simple mathematical model of waves to

- predict the behavior of a wave as it travels from one medium to another.

CONNECT
0.5 class period

📱 **APP** 15
Vocabulary App

👆 **INTERACTIVITY** 10
Reactive Ripples

LESSON 1 20
Student Edition

📖 **ETEXT** 20

NEXT GENERATION SCIENCE STANDARDS

MS-PS4-1 Use mathematical representations to describe a simple model for waves that includes how the amplitude of a wave is related to the energy in a wave.

DCI PS4.A Wave Properties A simple wave has a repeating pattern with a specific wavelength, frequency, and amplitude.

CCC.1 Patterns Graphs, charts, and images can be used to identify patterns in data.

SEP.5 Using Mathematics and Computational Thinking Use mathematical representations to describe and/or support scientific conclusions and design solutions.

Connection to Nature of Science Science knowledge is based upon logical and conceptual connections between evidence and explanations.

INVESTIGATE
1–3 class periods

🧪 *u*Investigate Lab 60
Waves and Their Characteristics

👆 INTERACTIVITY 15
Modeling Waves

👆 INTERACTIVITY 15
Making Waves

▶ VIDEO 5
Teaching Video

SYNTHESIZE
1–2 class periods

👆 INTERACTIVITY 15
Describe the Properties of Waves

👆 *Quest* CHECK-IN 10
Light Behavior

📄 DOCUMENT 15
L3 Enrichment

DEMONSTRATE
0.5 class period

LESSON 1 Check 15
Student Edition

☑ ASSESSMENT 30
Lesson Quiz

📄 DOCUMENT 15
L1 Remediation

LESSON FEATURE

Case Study 15
Sound and Light at the Ballpark

ELA/LITERACY STANDARDS

RH.6-8.7 Integrate visual information (e.g., in charts, graphs, photographs, videos, or maps) with other information in print and digital texts.

WHST.6-8.1.b Support claim(s) with logical reasoning and relevant, accurate data and evidence that demonstrate an understanding of the topic or text, using credible sources.

WHST.6-8.2.d Use precise language and domain-specific vocabulary to inform about or explain the topic.

MATHEMATICS STANDARDS

6.RP.A.2 Understand the concept of a unit rate a/b associated with a ratio $a:b$ with $b \neq 0$, and use rate language in the context of a ratio relationship. Expectations for unit rates in this grade are limited to non-complex fractions.

LESSON 1
Wave Properties

CONNECT

Objectives

Students will evaluate evidence and claims that
- different types of waves transmit energy in different ways.
- waves share common properties that influence the waves' behavior.

Students will analyze cause-and-effect relationships and determine how
- frequency, wavelength, and speed are related.

Students will use patterns described in a simple mathematical model of waves to
- predict the behavior of a wave as it travels from one medium to another.

Focus on Mastery!

Connect It! **SEP Engage in Argument** Have students form small groups and discuss the impacts that a tsunami (tidal wave) might have on a small community.

- Encourage them to think about the ways that a community might support its economy and get food. *(Because they are close to water, many communities affected by tsunamis rely on fishing).*
- Have students identify some of the challenges of repairing tsunami damage, including the costs of medical care and building supplies and the difficulty of getting building materials to some areas. Tsunamis can destroy roads and other means of transport or block them with debris, making reconstruction even more difficult.

A warning system enables residents to seek safety and shelter early and reinforce their homes and businesses, reducing the damage of the wave and making it easier to resume their regular lives.

NEXT GENERATION SCIENCE STANDARDS

MS-PS4-1 Use mathematical representations to describe a simple model for waves that includes how the amplitude of a wave is related to the energy in a wave.

Guiding Questions
- How can you use a simple model to describe a wave and its features?
- How can you observe the properties of waves?
- What kinds of patterns can you predict based on wave properties?

Connections
Literacy Integrate Information
Math Use Proportional Relationships

MS-PS4-1

HANDS-ON LAB

uInvestigate Model the three different types of mechanical waves.

Vocabulary
wave
mechanical wave
medium
electromagnetic radiation
transverse wave
amplitude
longitudinal wave
wavelength
frequency

Academic Vocabulary
vacuum

Connect It!

✏ **Read the caption, and then label the photos with different types of waves that are indicated in some way by the photos.**

SEP Engage in Argument How is Earth dependent on the sun for energy?

Sunlight is the primary source of energy for many processes on Earth, such as photosynthesis. The sun also provides the heat that many species need for survival.

Connect to Society How is a tsunami warning system a benefit to society?

It can alert people on shore that large, dangerous waves may be heading their way. Then, people can evacuate or take shelter.

PROFESSIONAL DEVELOPMENT

Content Refresher

Waves may be a combination of types. For example, waves at the surface of a body of deep water are mostly transverse. However, the waves closer to shore in shallower water are partially longitudinal, as friction with the shore slows down the bottom of the wave. The closer to shore the wave is, the greater the effect of the friction and the greater the longitudinal part of the wave. Combination waves that travel along the surface between two mediums are called *surface waves*. In the ocean, for example, surface waves travel at the surface between the water and the air. In surface waves, particles of the medium have a circular motion due to having both transverse and longitudinal wave components.

Types of Waves

When you think of a wave, you probably picture a surface wave on the ocean. Actually, a **wave** is any disturbance that transfers energy from place to place. An ocean wave is one type of wave called a **mechanical wave**, meaning it moves through some type of matter. The matter a wave travels through is called a **medium**. A mechanical wave cannot travel through a **vacuum**, such as space.

Sound waves are another type of mechanical wave. Sound can travel through the ocean, but it can also travel through a solid object, such as a piece of metal, or a gas, such as the air. It cannot travel through a vacuum such as space.

Another type of wave is an electromagnetic wave. This type of wave transfers **electromagnetic radiation**, a type of energy. Examples of electromagnetic radiation include visible light, radio waves, X-rays, and microwaves. Like a mechanical wave, electromagnetic waves transfer energy. However, electromagnetic waves are unique in that they can travel without a medium.

Both types of waves involve a transfer of energy without a transfer of matter. While mechanical waves travel *through* matter, the waves themselves do not move the matter to a new place. The waves are disturbances in matter that transfer energy.

Figure 1 shows several different types of waves at work. Ocean waves cause the buoy to bob in the water. If a seafloor sensor detects a wave called a tsunami (soo NAH mee), it sends a signal to the buoy, which then sends a radio signal to a satellite orbiting Earth. The signal gets relayed to scientists, who can then warn coastal communities. The sunlight that lights this scene is also made of waves.

Academic Vocabulary
A vacuum is completely empty. Why is the space around you not considered a vacuum?

It contains air, which is
made of matter.

 Reflect Write down some examples of waves that you are familiar with from everyday life. Can you classify them as mechanical or electromagnetic?

World of Waves
Figure 1 A tsunameter is a buoy anchored to the ocean floor. It detects extremely large waves called tsunamis and sends a radio signal to warn people.

electromagnetic radiation

mechanical wave

VOCABULARY APP

Students can practice lesson vocabulary throughout the lesson and before assessments.

INTERACTIVITY

GO ONLINE to access...
Reactive Ripples Students will explore the properties and characteristics of ripples as they change.

INVESTIGATE

Types of Waves

Connect to the Real World: Sound and Light Pollution As students identify mechanical and electromagnetic waves in everyday life, have them consider the effect that these waves have on humans and other organisms in the environment. Excessive sound waves, or sound pollution, can have a detrimental effect on quality of life by causing stress, while sound waves of excessive volume (i.e., amplitude) can damage hearing. Nighttime illumination can interfere with animal behavior and disrupt human sleep. Some cities have ordinances to control the levels of sound and light waves to reduce sound and light pollution.

Academic Vocabulary

Activate Prior Knowledge Ask students if and in what context they have heard the word *vacuum*. Students will most likely identify vacuum cleaners as an example of where they have heard the word. Ask students how they think vacuum cleaners might work, knowing the definition of *vacuum*.

 Reflect WHST.6-8.1.b
To get students started in their science notebooks, encourage them to think about the types of energy in the world around them and list which of those types are waves. Next, have them think about whether those waves are mechanical or electromagnetic and include that in their lists.

ELD SUPPORT

ELD.K12.ELL.SC.1

Writing Throughout the lesson, have students express ideas about waves using labeled sketches similar to those that accompany the text. Use these ideas to help them develop visual models to better understand waves.

Entering Draw diagrams of waves in water, ropes, and springs.

Beginning Draw diagrams and label wavelength and crest/trough or compression/rarefaction.

Developing Draw and label diagrams and write a few sentences to compare and contrast the properties of transverse and longitudinal waves.

Expanding Illustrate examples of transverse and longitudinal waves alongside labeled diagrams of these types of waves.

Bridging Create a written explanation of the relationship between wave properties shown in a labeled diagram and the equations relating frequency, wavelength, and wave speed.

INVESTIGATE

SCAFFOLDED QUESTIONS

Use the questions below to assess students' depth of understanding of the content on this page. Have students support their responses with evidence from the text.

Identify What are the types of waves? *(transverse waves, longitudinal waves, and surface waves)* **DOK 1**

Compare How do mechanical and electromagnetic waves differ? *(Both mechanical and electromagnetic waves transfer energy, but only mechanical waves require a medium.)* **DOK 2**

Teach with Visuals Use the following questions to guide students in learning from the image Transverse Waves:

- Where are the crest and the trough of each wave? Point these out on the image. *(The crest is the highest point, and the trough is the lowest point.)*
- What would happen if the person in the image moved his arms up and down faster? Slower? *(There would be more waves if he moved faster and fewer waves if he moved more slowly.)*

INTERACTIVITY

See how the energy and amplitude of a wave are related.

Transverse Waves

Figure 2 Use arrows to indicate the direction the rope is vibrating and the direction energy is flowing. Label a crest and a trough, and indicate the amplitude.

Transverse Waves Waves can be classified by how energy is transmitted. Energy is transmitted through a medium by mechanical waves. Electromagnetic waves are capable of transmitting energy through empty space.

Waves can also be classified by how the particles in a disturbance vibrate. A mechanical wave begins when a source of energy causes a medium to vibrate. The direction of the vibration determines what type of mechanical wave is produced. A **transverse wave** travels perpendicular (at right angles) to the direction of the source's motion. The person in **Figure 2** is using his arms to make up-and-down vibrations in two ropes. Each particle of the rope moves up and down. The direction of the waves he's producing, though, is perpendicular to that up-and-down motion. The energy travels toward the far ends of the ropes.

The curved shape of the rope indicates the main features of a transverse wave. The high point of a wave is its crest, and the low point is the trough. Halfway between the crest and trough is the wave's resting position. The distance between the highest crest and the resting position marks the wave's **amplitude**. In general, the amplitude of a wave is the maximum distance the medium vibrates from the rest position.

Electromagnetic waves, such as sunlight, are also transverse waves. In their case, however, there is no motion of particles, even when light travels through a liquid, such as water, or a solid, such as glass.

crest

amplitude

direction of vibration / motion

trough

direction of energy flow

PROFESSIONAL DEVELOPMENT

Develop Classroom Collaboration

When discussing or debating a topic in a classroom setting, it is important for students to feel comfortable speaking up with their opinions or ideas. Have students practice constructive critiques of classmates' ideas, asking questions that require the speaker to clarify and defend ideas with evidence, rather than simply stating that the speaker is wrong.

Longitudinal Waves

A wave that travels in the same direction as the vibrations that produce it is called a **longitudinal wave**. Sound is a longitudinal wave. Sound travels from speakers when flat surfaces inside the speakers vibrate in and out, compressing and expanding the air next to them.

Figure 3 shows a longitudinal wave in a spring toy. When the left hand pulls on the toy, the result is a series of stretches and compressions. Gaps between compressions are called rarefactions. Energy moves to the right along the toy.

While the wave travels, the spring particles do not move all the way to the right like the wave does. Each spring particle moves back and forth, like the hand. The small piece of ribbon on the spring moves the same way the particles in the spring move.

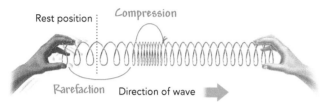

Rest position · *Compression*

Rarefaction · Direction of wave

Literacy Connection

Integrate Information As you learn about waves, take notes that summarize and categorize the different motions that waves produce.

Longitudinal Wave
Figure 3 ✏ Label a compression and a rarefaction.

Surface Waves

Combinations of transverse and longitudinal waves are called surface waves. For example, an ocean wave travels at the surface of water. When a wave passes through water, the water (and anything on it) vibrates up and down. The water also moves back and forth slightly in the direction that the wave is traveling. The up-and-down and back-and-forth movements combine to make each particle of water move in a circle, as shown in **Figure 4**.

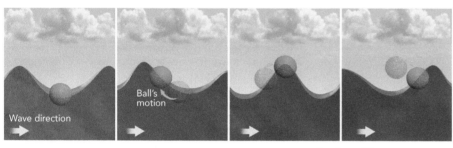

Wave direction

Ball's motion

☑ READING CHECK **Compare and Contrast** What is the main difference between a surface wave and a longitudinal wave?
Particlces in a surface wave move in two directions, while particles in a longitudinal wave move in just one direction.

Surface Wave
Figure 4 As waves move from left to right, they cause the ball to move in a circle.

7

Teach with Movement Have several students line up with their hands resting on the shoulders of the person in front of them. Gently but firmly push on the shoulders of the person at the back of the line and observe as the motion transfers through the rest of the people in the line. This is similar to the motion of a longitudinal wave.

Literacy Connection WHST.6-8.2.d

Integrate Information Remind students to…
- take notes in a variety of formats.
- include any sketches or graphs that can aid in their understanding of the material.
- categorize the information in their notes.

SYNTHESIZE

 **INTERACTIVITY**

GO ONLINE to access…
Describe the Properties of Waves Have students work individually to use this online activity and practice describing the properties of waves via an electronic simulation.

☑ READING CHECK **RH.6-8.7**

Compare and Contrast Guide students to compare the motions of the two waves, rather than their origins or shapes.

DIFFERENTIATED INSTRUCTION

L1 Support Struggling Students

Provide students with ample opportunities to visualize and experience transverse and longitudinal waves. Demonstrate both types of waves using a coiled spring and have students practice using the words *transverse* and *longitudinal* while observing each type of wave.

INVESTIGATE

Properties of Waves

Assess on the Spot Have students draw a quick sketch to show a wave with a comparatively deep trough and another wave with a comparatively shallow trough. Next, have them sketch a wave with a low frequency and another wave with a high frequency. This activity will help students answer the Guiding Question "How can you observe the properties of waves?"

HANDS-ON LAB

📄 **GO ONLINE to download...**

ᴎInvestigate

Waves and Their Characteristics Students use various materials to investigate wave characteristics. **Editable**

Class Time (60)

Group Size groups

Materials (per group) spring toy, shallow pan of water, narrow tape or ribbon, small floating toy, small stone, 3-m length of rope, meter stick, stopwatch

Procedure Tips Demonstrate movement of the spring toy to students prior to handing the toys out for the lab.

Properties of Waves
Figure 5 All waves have amplitude, wavelength, frequency, and speed. After you read about these properties, answer the questions on the image.

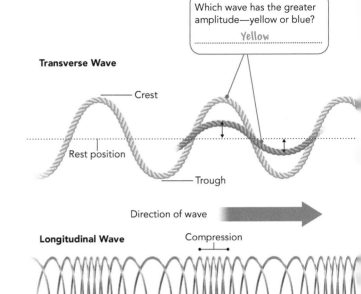

Which wave has the greater amplitude—yellow or blue?
Yellow

Transverse Wave

Crest

Rest position

Trough

Direction of wave

Longitudinal Wave

Compression

HANDS-ON LAB

ᴎInvestigate Model the three different types of mechanical waves.

👆 **INTERACTIVITY**

See how a wave travels through a coil.

Properties of Waves

In addition to amplitude, all waves have three other properties: wavelength, frequency, and speed. These properties are all related to one another.

Wavelength Suppose that a wave repeats as it travels. Its **wavelength** is determined by the distance it travels before it starts to repeat. The wavelength of a transverse wave is the distance from crest to crest, as shown in **Figure 5**. For a longitudinal wave, the wavelength is the distance from one compression to the next.

Frequency The number of times a wave repeats in a given amount of time is called its **frequency**. You can also think of frequency as the number of waves that pass a given point in a certain amount of time. For example, if you make waves on a rope so that one wave passes by a point every second, the frequency is 1 wave per second. Frequency is measured in units called hertz (Hz). A wave that occurs every second has a frequency of 1 Hz. If two waves pass by in a second, the frequency is 2 Hz.

PROFESSIONAL DEVELOPMENT

Beyond the Content

The highest frequency that humans can hear is about 20,000 Hz. (For comparison, bats can hear sounds up to 100,000 Hz.) The human ability to hear high frequencies generally degrades over time. A person's hearing range can also be impacted by hearing damage related to exposure to loud sounds. Listening to loud music or being near very loud noises, such as jet engines, can increase the rate of hearing loss.

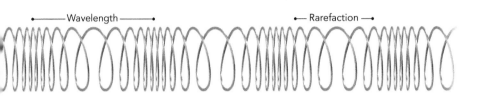

One yellow wave passes by this point each second, so the frequency of the yellow wave is __1 Hz__.

Two green waves pass by this point each second, so the frequency of the green wave is __2 Hz__.

Amplitude

Wavelength

Wavelength — Rarefaction —

Speed

The speed of a wave is determined by the distance it travels in a certain amount of time. Different waves have different speeds. For instance, a light wave travels almost a million times faster than a sound wave travels through air! Waves also travel at different speeds through different materials. For example, light travels faster through water than through glass. Sound travels more than three times faster through water than through air.

To calculate a wave's speed, divide the distance it travels by the time it takes to travel that distance. You can also find a wave's speed if you know its wavelength and frequency—just multiply wavelength times frequency.

Wave speed = Wavelength × Frequency

 INTERACTIVITY

Generate virtual waves in a wave pool.

✓ READING CHECK **Predict** If you and a friend are standing at opposite ends of a gymnasium and one of you claps, will the other person hear the clap at the same time she sees it happen? Why or why not?

No, because it takes more time for sound to reach our ears
than for the light from the event to travel to our eyes.

9

DIFFERENTIATED INSTRUCTION

L1 Support Struggling Students

Support students in understanding the difference between frequency and wavelength by thinking about the parts of the words. Frequency indicates how frequently a full wave passes by a point, and wavelength is related to the length, or distance, between the starting point of two consecutive waves.

L3 Support Advanced Students

Guide students in understanding the effect that the temperature of a medium has on the speed of a mechanical wave, such as sound. Have them research in small groups why temperature is an important factor when calculating sound wave characteristics.

 INTERACTIVITY

GO ONLINE to access...
Modeling Waves Students use mathematical representations to describe a simple model of waves.

What it is Models and data

What it does Allows students to explore the connection between wave behavior and patterns in behavior that can be predicted

How to use it
• Discuss with students how some patterns can be described by mathematical equations and that these patterns can be predicted.
• Have students review simple equations and their corresponding graphs to reinforce the connection between the two.
• Discuss how amplitude and energy are related.

Make Analogies To get students thinking about the relationship between frequency and energy, ask them to hold a tennis ball and squeeze it repeatedly but slowly for 15 seconds. Next, have them squeeze the same tennis ball repeatedly as quickly as they can for 15 seconds. Which seemed like it took more energy? Higher-frequency waves have higher energy. Students may rely on this analogy for the content to come.

 INTERACTIVITY

GO ONLINE to access...
Making Waves Have students work in small groups and use the activity to explore the connection between the wave characteristics and the use of the plunger. Have the groups select one student to take written notes and another to sketch the changes in wave shape.

✓ READING CHECK **WHST.6-8.1.b**

Predict Remind students that further observations can help them with their predictions.
• Review how sound travels in a wave.
• Have students discuss the different ways that waves travel depending on the medium.

LESSON 1

INVESTIGATE

Wave Energy

VIDEO

GO ONLINE to access...
Teaching Video Students delve deeper into a lesson concept.

 **6.RP.A.2**

Use Proportional Relationships Guide students as they complete the math activity.

• As a class, examine the relationship between wavelength and frequency and between wavelength and speed. Discuss as a class how the medium could influence these values.

SYNTHESIZE

DOCUMENT

GO ONLINE to download...
L3 Enrichment Extend student understanding of the lesson. **Editable**

NEXT GENERATION SCIENCE STANDARDS

MS-PS4-1 Use mathematical representations to describe a simple model for waves that includes how the amplitude of a wave is related to the energy in a wave.

VIDEO
See what happens when balls of different masses are dropped in water.

Wave Energy

Waves transmit energy from place to place. The amount of energy they transmit depends on how much energy was input by the original source of the vibration. Faster vibrations transmit more energy. Larger amplitude vibrations also transmit more energy.

In mathematical terms, a wave's energy is directly proportional to frequency. When the frequency of the wave doubles, the energy also doubles. So, if you shake a rope up and down twice as fast, you transmit twice as much energy down the length of the rope.

Mathematically, a wave's energy is also proportional to the square of its amplitude. For instance, if you shake a rope to make waves and then move your hand three times as high with each shake, the wave energy increases by a factor of 3 times 3, or nine! Like other forms of energy, a wave's energy is measured in units called joules (J).

Math Toolbox
Wave Properties

The table shows the properties of waves near the beach on one summer day. Use the relationship between speed, wavelength, and frequency to complete the table. Then answer the questions.

Waves at a Beach				
Time	Amplitude	Wavelength	Frequency	Speed
10 AM	0.4 m	10 m	2 Hz	20 m/s
2 PM	0.2 m	8 m	4 Hz	32 m/s
6 PM	0.3 m	12 m	3 Hz	34 m/s

1. Use Tables What would happen to the energy of the 10 AM wave if the frequency increased to 6 Hz?

   The wave energy would triple.

2. Apply Mathematics If the amplitude of the 6 PM wave increases to 0.6 m, how many times greater would the energy become?

   The energy would become 4 times greater.

3. Use Proportional Relationships Recall that speed = wavelength × frequency. Assuming that the wavelength of a wave stays the same, would the energy of the wave increase or decrease if the speed of the wave increases? Why?

   The energy would increase. Increasing speed while keeping wavelength the same would result in an increase of frequency. And increasing frequency increases energy.

PROFESSIONAL DEVELOPMENT

Reflect
Which activities in this lesson seemed to best promote students' understanding of waves?

Which aspects of wave properties and wave behavior seemed to require the most effort for students to comprehend?

Reflection, Refraction, and Absorption

If you've ever been to the beach, you've seen how different kinds of waves move. Some ocean waves crash into rocks or piers, while others reach the shore smoothly. Rays of sunlight hit the surface of the water, and some bounce off while others pass through. In general, when waves encounter different media, they are either reflected, transmitted, or absorbed.

Reflection Some waves are completely blocked by an obstruction, but their energy is not absorbed or converted to another form of energy. These types of waves bounce off, or reflect from, those obstructions. In a **reflection**, the wave bounces off and heads in a different direction. The law of reflection states that the angle of incidence equals the angle of reflection. This means that the angle at which the wave strikes the material will match the angle at which the reflected wave bounces off that material, as shown in **Figure 2**. Light reflecting from a mirror is the most familiar example of reflection. The echo of a voice from the walls of a canyon is another example.

Reflection
Figure 2 A flashlight beam reflects off of a mirror at the same angle it strikes.

a Angle of incidence The angle between the incoming wave and the normal.

b Normal A line perpendicular to the surface at the point where reflection occurs.

c Angle of reflection The angle between the reflected wave and the normal.

Fish Reflection and Refraction
Figure 1 Light waves reflecting off the walls of a tank can create multiple images of the same fish.

15

HANDS-ON LAB

📄 **GO ONLINE to download...**
Follow the Bouncing Ball Students will follow the angles that a ball makes as it strikes a wall and bounces off. **Editable**

INVESTIGATE

Reflection, Refraction, and Absorption

Activate Prior Knowledge Have students think about the last time that they hand-washed dishes or filled a bathtub. What happened to the water movement once it hit the side of the container? This is an example of waves reflecting off a solid surface.

ELD SUPPORT

ELD.K12.ELL.SC.1

Writing Design questions for students at different proficiency levels to help them access the main idea. Use these ideas to help support their understanding of wave interactions.

Entering Label diagrams of different types of wave interactions when analyzing information.

Beginning Record the results and observations from an investigation with a partner.

Developing Outline the steps of the investigation of wave interactions.

Expanding Describe the analytical procedures necessary to investigate wave interactions.

Bridging Explain, in detail, the connections between different types of wave interactions and the properties of the waves themselves.

LESSON 2

Academic Vocabulary

Spark a Discussion Have students form small groups. Within each group, have students select one person as the recorder. Give students 1 minute to write down as many words beginning with the prefix *trans-* as they can. After the minute is up, have students discuss what the words have in common.

Focus on Mastery!

Plan It! SEP Develop Models To assist students in this activity, have them work in pairs to experiment with different orientations of tape and mirrors. Have one student position the materials and then have the other student adjust the materials while the first student checks their orientation.

Address Misconceptions Students might think that refraction occurs due solely to a change in material. While it is true that refraction occurs during this type of transition, refraction is the result of a change in speed. Reinforce the idea that it is the change in speed that causes the bending and that materials with the same refractive index do not cause a bending of waves as light passes from one to another.

Plan It

SEP Develop Models ✏ Have you ever seen a movie scene in which a character appears to be looking at a mirror, yet the camera is not visible in the mirror? Think about how the director sets up this scene. Draw a set up that shows the position of the actor, the camera, and the mirror, and demonstrate why the camera's image is not visible to the camera.

Check student drawings to make sure the angle of incidence of the camera with respect to the mirror is large enough that the camera reflection is not visible but small enough so that the actor's image is visible.

Refraction

Figure 3 Light rays bend as they enter water because one side of the wave fronts slows down in water while the other side continues at the same speed in air.

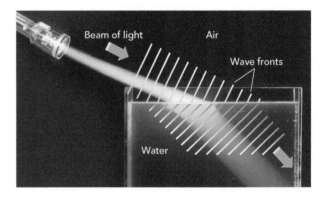

Academic Vocabulary

What is another way for saying that a wave is "transmitted" through a medium?

A wave passes through the medium.

Refraction Imagine riding a bike down a smooth asphalt road. When you turn off the road onto a dirt path, the transition can be jarring. You might have to grip the handlebars hard to keep the bike going straight as each wheel is on a different surface.

When light waves are **transmitted** from one medium into another, they also bend in different directions. This bending is due to **refraction**, or the bending of waves due to a change in speed.

When a wave enters a new medium at an angle other than perpendicular, it changes direction. For instance, when light is directed at water at an angle, as in **Figure 3**, the light slows down and bends downward. The wave bends toward the normal, the imaginary line that runs perpendicular from the boundary between the two media.

PROFESSIONAL DEVELOPMENT

Collaborate With the Community

Some communities and educational facilities host public "maker spaces," where participants can experiment with scientific tools and devices and create objects or technology. If a maker space exists in your area, collaborate with a representative to show students how waves and lenses play a role in projects that people are working on.

Diffraction Did you ever wonder how you can hear someone speaking even if they are around the corner of a building or doorway? This is an example of **diffraction**. Waves don't only travel in straight lines. They are also bend around objects.

You can observe diffraction with water waves as well as sound waves. Water waves can diffract around a rock or an island in the ocean. Because tsunami waves can diffract all the way around an island, people on the shores of the entire island are at risk.

Absorption When you think of something being absorbed, you might think of how a paper towel soaks up water. Waves can be absorbed by certain materials, too. In **absorption**, the energy of a wave is transferred to the material it encounters. When ocean waves reach a shoreline, most of their energy is absorbed by the shore.

When light waves encounter the surface of a different medium or material, the light waves may be reflected, refracted, or absorbed. What happens to the waves depends on the type of material they hit. Light is mostly absorbed by dark materials, such as the surface of a parking lot, and mostly reflected by light materials, such as snow.

Literacy Connection

Integrate Information
As you read, classify the phenomena you learn about as either interactions between waves and media or interactions among waves.

Reflect What are some ways in which you use reflection in your everyday life? Are there things you have to keep in mind when you use reflective devices, such as mirrors?

▶ **VIDEO**

Discover how reflection and absorption create echoes.

Question It!

Classify ✏ Identify each picture as being an example of reflection, refraction, or absorption.

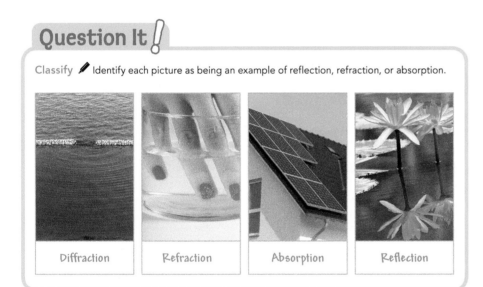

| Diffraction | Refraction | Absorption | Reflection |

DIFFERENTIATED INSTRUCTION

L1 Support Struggling Students
Support students in understanding the difference between diffraction, reflection, and refraction by guiding them in creating a visual organizer that shows a wave undergoing the various changes.

L3 Support Advanced Students
Challenge students by asking them to describe a scenario in which reflection and diffraction occur. Then have them sketch out the paths of the waves, the changes in wave direction, and the parts of the setup necessary for their scenario to occur.

Literacy Connection SL.7.5

Integrate Information Encourage students to...
• organize their observations in multimedia formats, such as digital slides.

Address Misconceptions Students might think that when a wave goes through a gap or around a barrier, it terminates completely and reforms as another type of wave. Reinforce the idea that the waves can actually change shape, bending around barriers and moving through openings rather than stopping and reforming. The wave continues without stopping because the particles on one side of the opening or barrier are still transmitting energy to the particles on the other side.

Reflect WHST.6-8.2.b

Have students write in their science notebooks about times that they use mirrors and other reflective surfaces. Recall the Guiding Question "How do waves interact with different materials?" Many students will think of looking at themselves in a mirror but encourage them to think of less obvious uses, such as checking traffic in a rearview mirror or using devices that contain mirrors.

▶ **VIDEO**

GO ONLINE to access...
Teaching Video Students delve deeper into a lesson concept.

🔍 Focus on Mastery!

Question It! Classify To assist students in this activity, have students volunteer to sketch the different scenarios on the board. Have another student trace the path of a wave through the sketch and discuss as a class what happens as it moves through different materials.

LESSON 2

Wave Interference

HANDS-ON LAB

📄 **GO ONLINE to download...**

Investigate

Standing Waves and Wave Interference
Students work in groups to model interference using a long spring toy. They model resonance by making standing waves in a rope. In each case, students explore the effect of variables such as wave speed and amplitude on the behavior of the waves and record their observations using words and drawings.
Editable

Class Time (25)

Group Size groups

Materials (per group) spring toy, meter stick

📄 **GO ONLINE to download**
the materials kit list.

Procedure Tips
- Arrange to conduct the lab in an open area such as a hallway to allow for adequate floor space for all student groups.
- Remind students to handle the springs carefully to avoid stretching or tangling them.
- Caution students to use care when pulling back the spring toy and to keep the toy clear of their faces.
- If time allows, permit students to experiment with different types of wave movements using the spring toy. Remind them to write down their observations.

HANDS-ON LAB

Investigate See what type of interference you get when you send waves down a coil.

Wave Interference
Have you ever seen two ocean waves collide from opposite directions so they momentarily form a bigger, hill-like shape before continuing in their original directions? This is an example of wave **interference**. There are two types.

Constructive Interference The example of two waves of similar sizes colliding and forming a wave with an amplitude greater than either of the original waves is called constructive interference. You can think of it as waves "helping each other," or adding their energies together. As shown in **Figure 4**, when the crests of two waves overlap, they make a higher crest. If two troughs overlap, they make a deeper trough. In both cases, the amplitude of the combined crests or troughs increases.

Types of Interference
Figure 4 ✏️ Write captions to describe three parts of destructive interference. Complete the key to explain what the different arrows mean in the images.

Constructive Interference

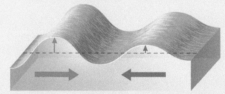

❶ Two waves approach each other. The wave on the left has a greater amplitude.

❷ The new crest's amplitude is the sum of the amplitudes of the original crests.

Destructive Interference

❶ Two waves with equal amplitudes approach each other.

❷ The crest of one wave overlaps the trough of the other wave and they cancel out.

PROFESSIONAL DEVELOPMENT

Beyond the Content
One reason that tsunamis can be so devastating is that waves in the deep ocean can interact via constructive interference. When these waves combine, they become massively powerful. Waves of this size can overcome protective measures constructed by residents near bodies of water, and they have the ability to cause extreme amounts of damage to nearby areas.

Destructive Interference When two waves combine to form a wave with a smaller amplitude than either original wave had, this is called destructive interference. Destructive interference occurs when the crest of one wave overlaps the trough of another wave. If the crest has a larger amplitude than the trough of the other wave, the crest "wins," and part of it remains. If the original trough has a larger amplitude than the crest of the other wave, the result is a trough. If a crest and trough have equal amplitudes, they cancel each other out, as shown in **Figure 4**. Destructive interference is used in noise-canceling headphones to block out distracting noises in a listener's surroundings.

✅ **READING CHECK** **Infer** Which type of wave interference could cause sound to become louder? Explain your answer.

Constructive interference; the waves interfere such that the crests overlap and the amplitudes add together.

Interfering Waves
Figure 5 Ripples created by rain water on a pond interfere with one another in a pattern that exhibits both constructive and destructive interference.

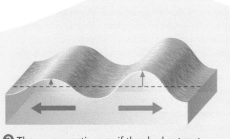

❸ The waves continue as if they had not met.

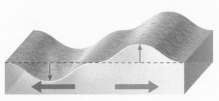

❸ *The waves continue as if they had not met.*

Key
→ direction of Wave 1
← direction of Wave 2
↑ amplitude of Wave 1
↓ amplitude of Wave 2

19

🖐 **INTERACTIVITY**

GO ONLINE to access...
Model Wave Interactions Students develop and use a model to describe how waves are reflected, absorbed, or transmitted through various materials.

What it is Models and data

What it does Allows students to explore the interactions between waves and materials

How to use it

• Discuss with students that waves move differently through different materials.
• Have students think about different types of waves and the materials through which they might move.
• Assist students in drawing diagrams that can help model wave behavior.

Teach with Movement Have students model the different types of wave interference by breaking the class into two groups and having students in each group link hands in a long line. Have them act out constructive and destructive interference as you go over the characteristics of this behavior and instruct their movement. This activity will help students answer the Guiding Question, "How do waves interact with each other?"

✅ **READING CHECK** **WHST.6-8.1.b**

Infer Guide students in using the diagrams to make inferences about wave behavior.

• Review what constructive and destructive interference look like.
• Have students review which property of waves affects the loudness of sound.

NOTES

LESSON 2

Teach with Visuals Guide students in learning from the visual **Standing Waves**:

• How many antinodes do you predict will appear in the rope when there are two wavelengths? *(four)*

• How are the nodes similar in all three examples? *(The nodes appear to hold still.)*

• How does the wavelength of the standing waves change as the frequency increases? Describe the pattern you observe. *(As frequency increases, the wavelength decreases.)*

• Why is it important to hold one end of the rope still in order to produce standing waves? *(Interference from reflected waves leads to standing waves. If one end isn't held still, then there will be no reflected waves.)*

Standing Waves

Figure 6 As the hand shown at left increases the frequency, the number of wavelengths present in the standing wave will increase. In a standing wave, it looks like there's a mirror image of both the crest and trough. Label the rest of the nodes and antinodes.

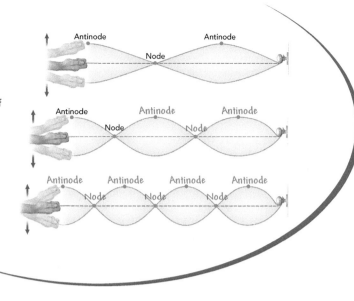

INTERACTIVITY

Describe how waves behave when they interact with a barrier or boundary.

Standing Waves Look at the rope setup in **Figure 6.** The rope is tied to a doorknob, and someone shakes the free end. This motion can generate standing waves. A **standing wave** is a wave that appears to stand in one place. Standing waves are produced by two waves interfering with each other as they travel in opposite directions. Standing waves on the rope appear when an incoming wave and wave reflected from the doorknob have just the right frequency to interfere as shown.

In a standing wave, destructive interference between the two colliding waves produces points with zero amplitude, called nodes. The nodes are always evenly spaced along the wave. Points of maximum amplitude on a standing wave are called antinodes. Antinodes always occur halfway between two nodes. The frequency and wavelength of the interfering waves determine how many nodes and antinodes the standing wave will have. When seen in real life, the antinodes appear to pulse in and out from the rope's rest position while the nodes appear motionless.

Standing waves can sometimes appear on lakes when the wind and pressure around them are just right. The water appears to have a node in the center of the lake, and the water wave rolls around that node.

PROFESSIONAL DEVELOPMENT

Reflect

How can you help students to make connections between the content of the topic and other parts of your curriculum?

....

....

Resonance Think about the last time you swung on a swing at a playground. You may have noticed that it is difficult to get yourself going. Once you are in motion, you can pull on the chains of the swing and pump your legs at the right time to keep yourself swinging. The swing has a natural frequency, and your actions match that frequency to create greater amplitudes in your motion.

Most objects have at least one natural frequency of vibration. Standing waves occur in an object when it vibrates at one of these natural frequencies. If a nearby object vibrates at the same frequency, it can cause resonance. **Resonance** is an increase in the amplitude of a vibration that occurs when external vibrations match an object's natural frequency.

When engineers build a bridge, they have to make sure that bridge supports are not placed at potential nodes for a standing wave. Otherwise, wind could cause the bridge to swing wildly like the rope in **Figure 6** and collapse.

Understanding the resonance of different materials is also useful for people who build guitars, violins, or other wood-based stringed instruments. If the wood in a guitar, such as the one in **Figure 7**, resonates too much with a certain note, it may sound too loud when that particular note is struck. Likewise, if the wood does not resonate with any particular note, the instrument may lack volume or "presence" and sound dull.

☑ READING CHECK **Summarize** In general, why is it risky to build something whose natural frequency can be matched by external vibrations?
The amplitude of the waves in the object can be increased to the point of damage to the object, or sound that is too loud or harsh.

 Make Meaning Make a two-column chart in your notebook. Use it to record descriptions of constructive interference, destructive interference, standing waves, and resonance.

Musical Resonance
Figure 7 The types of wood and construction techniques used to make a guitar affect aspects of its sound, including its resonance.

 21

DIFFERENTIATED INSTRUCTION

L1 Support Struggling Students
Discuss with students the meaning of the prefix *anti-* and assist students in applying this concept to the study of standing waves. Remind them that at the node, no particle motion is occurring. At the antinode (or "opposite of the node"), the most particle motion is occurring in a standing wave.

L3 Support Advanced Students
Have students research one example of resonance that involves sound waves. Two good examples are what happens when a wine glass resonates with a musical note and what happens when a bottle makes a noise when someone blows over the opening.

SCAFFOLDED QUESTIONS

Use the questions below to assess students' depth of understanding of the content on this page. Have students support their responses with evidence from the text.

Identify Give some examples of objects that are affected by resonance. (*pushing someone on a swing, a string instrument vibrating*) **DOK 1**

Compare How is a playground swing like a bridge when it comes to resonance? (*Both objects can resonate when waves match their natural frequencies.*) **DOK 2**

☑ READING CHECK **WHST.6-8.1.b**

Summarize Guide students in summarizing the risks of resonance on buildings and other constructed items.
• Review what happens during resonance.
• Ask students to infer how the effects of resonance, such as the effects on the Tacoma Narrows Bridge, might also affect other types of construction.

SYNTHESIZE

👆 **INTERACTIVITY**

GO ONLINE to access...
Use Models to Describe Wave Behavior Students will explore changes in wave behavior using simulations.

📄 **DOCUMENT**

GO ONLINE to download...
L3 Enrichment Extend student understanding of the lesson. **Editable**

☑ LESSON 2 Check

☑ LESSON 2 Check

MS-PS4-2

Quest CHECK-IN

👆 INTERACTIVITY

GO ONLINE to access...
Virtual Optics Using an online simulation, students experiment with mirrors and lenses to simulate changes in light. They review the concepts of diffraction, reflection, and refraction while navigating a virtual obstacle course and direct light at a target.

DEMONSTRATE

Assessment and Remediation

 ASSESSMENT

GO ONLINE to access...
Lesson Quiz Formally assess students' learning from the lesson using this auto-graded online assessment. **Editable**

📄 DOCUMENT

GO ONLINE to download...
L1 Remediation This auto-assigned remediation document provides targeted support for students who struggle on the assessment. **Editable**

Depth of Knowledge

DOK Level	Questions	DOK Level	Questions
1	1, 2	3	4
2	3		

---

1. CCC Cause and Effect Explain what happens to light when it is refracted at the surface of water.

The light is bent as it changes speed when it moves through a different medium.

2. SEP Interpret Data The diagrams below show two waves interfering to form a dark blue result. Which of the diagrams depicts constructive interference? Explain your choice using the term *amplitude*.

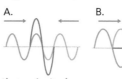

Choice A. It shows waves approaching each other and their amplitudes combining to form a wave of larger amplitude in the middle as the waves pass through each other.

3. Explain What does it mean for waves to be absorbed by a certain medium? Make sure to include energy in your explanation.

The energy of the wave is transferred to that medium or material.

4. SEP Construct Explanations Why does the transition of light waves from water to air make it seem as if fish and other things in a pond are shallower than they actually are?

This is due to refraction. Light that reflects off the fish bends as it exits the water and travels to a person's eyes, due to the different speeds of light in the two media.

Quest CHECK-IN

In this lesson, you learned how waves interact with their surroundings and with each other. Waves can reflect, refract, and be absorbed depending on the media they travel through and the materials they strike. They can also interfere with each other in ways that are destructive or constructive, resulting in phenomena such as standings waves and resonance.

SEP Design Solutions Think about the ways that light can change direction. What are two ways that you could change the path of light? What materials would you need to do it?

You could refract it or reflect it. Refract it by passing it through water or glass; reflect it with a mirror.

👆 INTERACTIVITY

Virtual Optics

Go online to experiment with light and its transmission or reflection.

Lesson Check Scoring Notes
Assess students' responses using the rubrics below:

3. Explain DOK 2, 2 points

1pt	Student states that the wave's energy is transferred to the medium.
1pt	Student explains his or her answer.

4. SEP Construct Explanations DOK 3, 2 points

1pt	Student recognizes the role of refraction.
1pt	Student describes the role of speed in diffraction.

NEXT GENERATION SCIENCE STANDARDS

MS-PS4-2 Develop and use a model to describe that waves are reflected, absorbed, or transmitted through various materials.

MS-PS4-2

littleBits
CHALLENGE

Say "CHEESE!"

VIDEO
Find out how cameras work.

For hundreds of years, people who traveled took sketch pads and pencils to record their memories. This all changed in the nineteenth century with the invention of photography.

The Challenge To continue to improve the ways in which people can record images.

Phenomenon Early cameras were large and clumsy objects that printed images on glass. In the twentieth century, engineers experimented with smaller and lighter cameras that used film. Today we have digital cameras. But they all use the same process to create images.

Cameras have changed a lot over the years!

Today, cameras all have three main parts for capturing light:

- The **lens** is the camera's eye. It detects the light reflected off of what you want to photograph.

- The **aperture** lets light in through the lens. The wider the aperture, the more light is let in.

- The **shutter** is like a curtain that opens when you take the photo.

In a film camera, the light changes the film both physically and chemically to create an image. In a *digital* camera, the light reaches photosensors, which convert the image to a string of numbers.

DESIGN CHALLENGE

Can you build your own simple camera using just a box? Go to the Engineering Design Notebook to find out!

23

littleBits
CHALLENGE

Go online to access your digital course for student activities and teacher support.

If your students enjoyed this activity, then encourage them to explore and investigate the littleBits challenges in their digital course. These unique opportunities allow students to continue their study of the engineering design process using littleBits electronic building blocks.

VIDEO

GO ONLINE to access...
Engineering Video Students see how engineers use science to develop a real-world solution.

DESIGN CHALLENGE | **Go to the Engineering Design Notebook**

Using Phenomena Students work in teams to build pinhole cameras using limited materials in a limited amount of time. Students test and refine their cameras.

Class Time (20)

Group Size groups

Materials (per group) aluminum foil, shoe box or small cardboard box, waxed paper, dark paper or fabric, scissors, pin

Safety
Take care when cutting aluminum foil. Do not place the pins near the eyes or mouth and handle them only by the dull end.

Advanced Prep (15)
Cut the pieces of aluminum foil into small squares. Have tape handy in case students need help securing their cameras together.

Classroom Strategies
- Pass around an inexpensive film camera so students can see the mechanisms more closely. If an older film camera is available for students to observe, place one on a table at the front of the classroom.
- Guide students in identifying the main functional parts of a camera and what items might make good models for these parts. Assist them in creating a two-column chart with which to organize these notes.

OBJECTIVES

CONNECT
0.5 class period

Students will develop and use models to explain how

- sound waves interact with matter by processes of reflection, absorption, transmittal, and diffraction.

Students will describe how

- stiffness, density, and temperature of materials affect the speed of sound.

📱 **APP** .... (15)
Vocabulary App

🧪 **HANDS-ON LAB** .... (10)
Amplitude and Loudness

LESSON 3 .... (20)
Student Edition

📖 **ETEXT** .... (20)

NEXT GENERATION SCIENCE STANDARDS

MS-PS4-2 Develop and use a model to describe that waves are reflected, absorbed, or transmitted through various materials.

DCI PS4.A Wave Properties A sound wave needs a medium through which is transmitted.

CCC.6 Structure and Function Structures can be designed to serve particular functions by taking into account properties of different materials, and how materials can be shaped and used.

SEP.2 Developing and Using Models Develop and/or use a model to predict and/or describe phenomena.

INVESTIGATE
1–2 class periods

INTERACTIVITY .... (20)
Reflection, Transmission, and Absorption of Sound Waves

Investigate Lab .... (30)

Understanding Sound

VIDEO .... (5)
Teaching Video

INTERACTIVITY .... (5)
Sound

SYNTHESIZE
1 class period

INTERACTIVITY .... (20)
Doppler Effect

DOCUMENT .... (15)
L3 Enrichment

DEMONSTRATE
0.5 class period

LESSON 3 Check .... (15)
Student Edition

ASSESSMENT .... (30)
Lesson Quiz

DOCUMENT .... (15)
L1 Remediation

ELA/LITERACY STANDARDS

RST.6-8.4 Determine the meaning of symbols, key terms, and other domain-specific words and phrases as they are used in a specific scientific or technical context relevant to grades 6–8 texts and topics.

RST.6-8.7 Integrate quantitative or technical information expressed in words in a text with a version of that information expressed visually.

MATHEMATICS STANDARDS

MP.2 Reason abstractly and quantitatively.

LESSON 3
Sound Waves

CONNECT

Objectives

Students will develop and use models to explain how
- sound waves interact with matter by processes of reflection, absorption, transmittal, and diffraction.

Students will describe how
- stiffness, density, and temperature of materials affect the speed of sound.

Focus on Mastery!

Connect It! SEP Engage in Argument
Support students in gaining mastery in answering and asking questions about science phenomena.

- Have several student volunteers describe the main characteristics of mechanical waves and electromagnetic waves. Write down or project the descriptions so that everyone can see them. Then have students pair up and use those descriptions to determine what kind of wave sound is.
- Have students pair up with new partners and develop a list of three other questions about sound. Tell students to think of specific questions related to properties of sound, how sound interacts with matter, and how sound travels.

NEXT GENERATION SCIENCE STANDARDS

MS-PS4-2 Develop and use a model to describe that waves are reflected, absorbed, or transmitted through various materials.

LESSON 3 Sound Waves

Guiding Questions
- How are sound waves reflected, transmitted, or absorbed by materials?
- What factors affect the speed of sound waves?

Connections
Literacy Integrate With Visuals
Math Reason Quantitatively

MS-PS4-2

HANDS-ON LAB

Investigate Use models to examine how sound waves travel through different media.

Vocabulary	Academic Vocabulary
loudness	differentiate
intensity	
decibel	
pitch	
Doppler effect	

Connect It!

✏ **When someone strikes a cymbal, the cymbal vibrates to produce sound. Draw compressions and rarefactions of the air particles as the sound waves travel away from the cymbal.**

SEP Engage in Argument Is sound a mechanical wave or an electromagnetic wave? Explain your answer.

Sound is a mechanical wave. It requires a medium to travel through.

CCC Cause and Effect What do you think happens to a sound wave when the volume of sound increases?

The amplitude of the wave increases.

PROFESSIONAL DEVELOPMENT

Content Refresher

Lesson 3 is about sound waves, mechanical longitudinal waves created by vibrations in gases, liquids, and solids.

- Like other mechanical waves, sound waves travel only through matter, not through vacuum.
- The stiffer and less compressible the matter, the faster sound travels through it. Sound travels faster through solids than liquids and faster through liquids than gases. The warmer the matter, the faster the sound travels.
- The amplitude of a sound wave corresponds to loudness. The frequency of a sound wave corresponds to pitch.
- A common sound wave phenomenon related to frequency is the Doppler effect, which is a shift in wave frequency that occurs when there is relative motion of the wave source and detector.

The Behavior of Sound

All sound waves begin with a vibration. Look at the woman in **Figure 1.** When she hits a drum or a cymbal with her drumstick, the drum or cymbal vibrates rapidly, disturbing the air particles around the drum set. When the drum or cymbal moves away from its rest position, it creates a compression by pushing air particles together. When it moves back toward its rest position, it creates a rarefaction by causing air particles to spread out.

Recall that sound waves are mechanical waves that require a medium through which to travel. In the case of the drummer and the drum set, the compressions and rarefactions that are created travel through the air. Sound waves, however, travel more easily through liquids and solids. When you set a glass down on a table, for example, the sound waves that are generated travel first through the glass and the table and then are released into the air.

Sound waves are also longitudinal—they travel in the same direction as the vibrations that produce them. Like other types of mechanical waves, sound waves can be reflected, transmitted, absorbed, and diffracted.

HANDS-ON LAB

Discover how the amplitude of a guitar string affects its loudness.

Making Waves
Figure 1 The vibrations caused by hitting drums and cymbals generate sound waves.

 VOCABULARY APP

Students can practice lesson vocabulary throughout the lesson and before assessments.

 **HANDS-ON LAB**

 GO ONLINE to download...
Amplitude and Loudness Students will pluck a guitar string to determine how amplitude is related to loudness. **Editable**

INVESTIGATE

The Behavior of Sound

Activate Prior Knowledge Have students answer the following questions: How are sounds made? How does sound get from its source to your ears?

Connect to the Real World: Music Therapy Sound in the form of music has a strong connection with the brain. Scientists studying the brain have found that when people hear music, the parts of their brain responsible for control of movement, emotions, and creativity become activated. Brain scientists have also found that the brain is more plastic—which means able to change—than once thought. Because of these new discoveries, music has become an important form of therapy for brain disorders. Have each student write down one or more examples from their own experience of how music has stimulated movement, emotions, or creativity in them. Pair up students, and have them share their examples.

Make Analogies Sound travels through air by *compressions* and *rarefactions*. Explain and illustrate these terms, and then demonstrate an analogy of a sound wave by showing a longitudinal wave traveling through a spring.

ELD SUPPORT

ELD.K12.ELL.SC.1

Speaking Have students verbally explain concepts related to the interactions of sound waves with matter.

Entering Have students name the four interactions of sound waves with matter: *transmission, reflection, absorption,* and *diffraction.*

Beginning Have students explain what *transmission, reflection, absorption,* and *diffraction* mean.

Developing Have students describe real-world examples of *transmission, reflection, absorption,* and *diffraction.*

Expanding Have students describe the kinds of materials that allow sound waves to undergo *transmission, reflection, absorption,* and *diffraction.*

Bridging Have students explain how they would draw models of *transmission, reflection, absorption,* and *diffraction.*

INVESTIGATE

Address Misconceptions Students may have many misconceptions about sound waves. Two common misconceptions about the transmission of sound are that sound can only travel through air and that sound cannot travel through opaque objects. Have students pair up and test whether sound can travel through an opaque solid. Have one student in each pair tap the solid material of a table or desk gently while the other student listens first through the air and then through the solid material by pressing an ear down on the table or desk. Then have students switch and repeat the test. Have students share what they learned.

Connect to the Real World: Noise in the Workplace Exposure to loud or random noise while working is a major hazard in many workplaces. High noise levels can cause hearing loss, stress, and distraction and interfere with communication and warning signals. Some employers give protective earplugs to workers. However, this is not an option in most workplaces because workers need to communicate. Installing quieter equipment and structures that reduce noise is the most effective way to reduce noise levels in the workplace. Revisit the Guiding Question, "How are sound waves reflected, transmitted, or absorbed by materials?" Have a discussion with the class about how these behaviors of sound can be applied to a structure designed to reduce noise. Then have students create a labeled drawing of a structure designed to reduce noise. Have students show in their drawings how sound interacts with the structure.

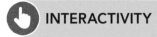 INTERACTIVITY

GO ONLINE to access...
Reflection, Transmission, and Absorption of Sound Waves This interactivity helps to activate prior knowledge. Students will explore the diffraction, absorption, transmission, and reflection of sound waves in everyday situations.

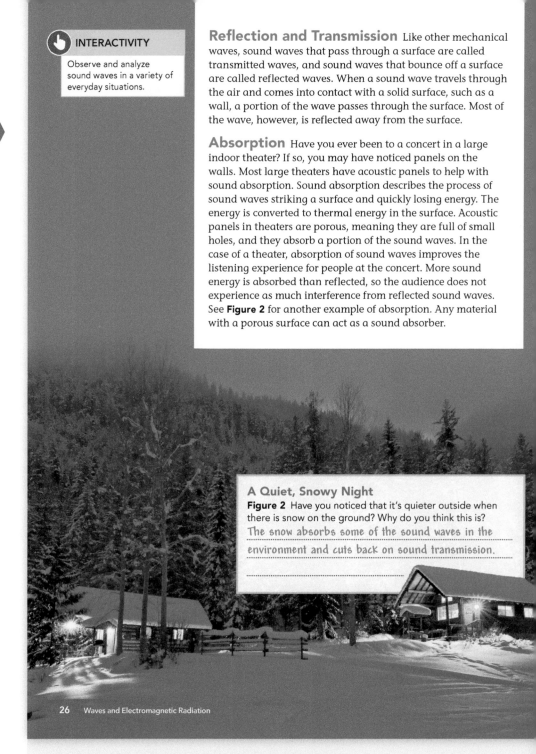

INTERACTIVITY

Observe and analyze sound waves in a variety of everyday situations.

Reflection and Transmission Like other mechanical waves, sound waves that pass through a surface are called transmitted waves, and sound waves that bounce off a surface are called reflected waves. When a sound wave travels through the air and comes into contact with a solid surface, such as a wall, a portion of the wave passes through the surface. Most of the wave, however, is reflected away from the surface.

Absorption Have you ever been to a concert in a large indoor theater? If so, you may have noticed panels on the walls. Most large theaters have acoustic panels to help with sound absorption. Sound absorption describes the process of sound waves striking a surface and quickly losing energy. The energy is converted to thermal energy in the surface. Acoustic panels in theaters are porous, meaning they are full of small holes, and they absorb a portion of the sound waves. In the case of a theater, absorption of sound waves improves the listening experience for people at the concert. More sound energy is absorbed than reflected, so the audience does not experience as much interference from reflected sound waves. See **Figure 2** for another example of absorption. Any material with a porous surface can act as a sound absorber.

A Quiet, Snowy Night
Figure 2 Have you noticed that it's quieter outside when there is snow on the ground? Why do you think this is?
The snow absorbs some of the sound waves in the environment and cuts back on sound transmission.

PROFESSIONAL DEVELOPMENT

Beyond the Content
Designing a concert hall for the ideal listening experience can be complicated because the designer wants to include some reflected sound. Designers know that too much reflected sound can be disorienting but the right amount of reflected sound at the right time provides a feeling of being enveloped by the music. An analysis of existing venues has led to the conclusion that a "shoe box" shape is ideal. Sound is reflected from the walls to the ears of each listener. Buildings with curved walls, such as fan, circular, and elliptical buildings, create spots where some listeners hear too much reflected sound and some too little. New concert halls now include walls between sections to provide the ideal listening experience for everyone.

Model It

If you've ever yelled loudly into an open space, such as a canyon or a courtyard, then you may have heard an echo. An echo occurs when sound waves are reflected off a hard surface, such as the wall of a rocky mountain. The sound you hear is delayed because it takes time for the sound waves to reflect off the surface and reach your ears.

SEP Develop Models ✏️ Draw a picture of sound waves when an echo is created. In addition to reflected waves, your model should also indicate waves that are transmitted or absorbed.

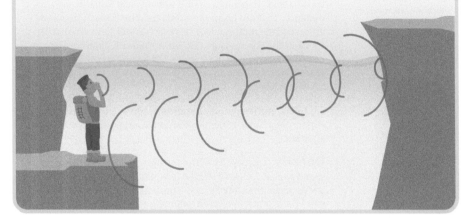

Diffraction It is usually easy to hear someone talking if they are in the same room as you, but you can also hear people in other rooms nearby. Why is this? You can hear them because sound waves can bend around the edges of an opening, such as a doorway. This is called sound diffraction. Sound waves, like water waves, spread out after passing through an opening.

How much sound waves are transmitted, reflected, absorbed, or diffracted depends greatly upon the medium through which they travel. If sound waves travel through air and hit a solid surface, such as a concrete wall, much of the energy in the waves is reflected back toward the source. If the surfaces they hit are softer or more porous, then more sound waves will be absorbed. Sound waves will be diffracted around corners and through passageways between hard surfaces.

 HANDS-ON LAB

ʊInvestigate Use models to examine how sound waves travel through different media.

✅ **READING CHECK** **Summarize** What are four things that can happen to sound waves when they reach a barrier?

They can be reflected, transmitted, absorbed, or diffracted.

27

LESSON 3

Factors Affecting the Speed of Sound

SCAFFOLDED QUESTIONS

Use the questions below to assess students' depth of understanding of the content on this page. Have students support their responses with evidence from the text.

Identify What four aspects of materials affect the speed of sound? *(compressibility, stiffness, density, and temperature)* **DOK 1**

Relate How does state of matter relate to the compressibility of a material? *(Solids are less compressible than liquids, and liquids are less compressible than gases.)* **DOK 2**

Model In materials with the same stiffness, why does sound travel faster through materials that are less dense? *(Less dense materials have less mass per unit of volume, so they accelerate more from energy disturbances than denser materials do. As a result, sound waves travel faster through less dense materials.)* **DOK 2**

Apply A company is making a device that will calculate distance by measuring the time it takes sound to echo in air. The device will be used to position a working robot. The company already makes sonar devices that calculate distance by measuring the time it takes sound to echo in water. Can the company reuse the sonar device as is for the robots? Why or why not? *(No, a new device will have to be made. The speed of sound is not the same in water and in air, and calculations of distance must take that into account.)* **DOK 3**

✅ **READING CHECK** **RST6-8.4**

Hypothesize Remind students to...
- identify the factor that describes the difference between air at the equator and air at the North Pole.
- explain how this factor will affect the speed of sound.

▶ **VIDEO**
Explore what thunder is and how to determine your distance from an approaching storm.

Speed of Sound
Figure 3 Rate the speed of sound through the medium in each container, with "1" being the fastest and "3" being the slowest.

Factors Affecting the Speed of Sound

As you have read, sound waves are mechanical waves that require a medium through which to travel. The characteristics of the medium have an effect on the speed of the sound waves traveling through them. The main factors that affect the speed of sound are compressibility, stiffness, density, and temperature.

Stiffness In general, sound waves travel faster in materials that are harder to compress. This is because of how efficiently the movement of one particle will push on another. Think of the coins, water, and air in **Figure 3**. Solids are less compressible than liquids, which are less compressible than gases. Therefore, sound waves travel fastest in solids and slowest in gases.

For solids, stiffness is also important. Sound travels faster in stiffer solids, such as metals, than in less rigid solids, such as pudding.

Density The density of the medium also affects the speed of sound waves. Density refers to how much matter or mass there is in a given amount of space. The denser the material, the more mass it has in a given volume, so the greater its inertia. Objects with greater inertia accelerate less from an energy disturbance than objects with less inertia, or less massive objects. Therefore, in materials of the same stiffness, sound travels more slowly in the denser material.

Temperature The temperature of a medium also affects the speed at which sound waves travel through it, though in more complicated ways. For solids, an increase in temperature reduces the stiffness, so the sound speed decreases. For fluids, such as air, the increase in temperature reduces the density, so the sound speed generally increases.

✅ **READING CHECK** **Hypothesize** Would sound waves travel slower through air at the North Pole or at the equator? Explain.
<u>Sound waves would travel slower in the air at the North Pole,</u>
<u>since it is much colder there than at the equator and sound</u>
<u>waves in air travel more slowly at lower temperatures.</u>

PROFESSIONAL DEVELOPMENT

Beyond the Content
Sound can reflect from some materials, and the speed of sound is constant in a specific material. These properties of sound make it ideal for visualization in water. People use sonar, which stands for sound navigation and ranging to "see" marine objects and the shape of the ocean floor. There are two kinds of sonar devices. Active sonar transmits high-frequency sound above 20,000 Hz, called ultrasound, and receives the ultrasound echo that comes back. The time it takes an echo to come back is used to determine the distance the sound wave traveled, and computer software produces an image from the distance calculations. Passive sonar does not transmit sound but does detect sound from objects such as ships, submarines, and large marine mammals. A similar process is used in medical facilities to "see" inside the human body with ultrasound.

Loudness and Pitch

How might you describe a sound? You might call it loud or soft, high or low. When you turn up the volume of your speakers, you increase the loudness of a sound. When you sing higher and higher notes, you increase the pitch of your voice. Loudness and pitch depend on different properties of sound waves.

Factors Affecting Loudness You use the term **loudness** to describe your awareness of the energy of a sound. How loud a sound is depends on the energy and intensity of the sound waves. If someone knocks lightly on your front door, then you might hear a quiet sound. If they pound on your door, then you hear a much louder sound. Why? The pounding transfers much more energy through the door than a light knock does. That's because a hard knock on a door produces a much greater amplitude in the sound waves than a softer knock does. Increased energy results in greater intensity of the waves. **Intensity** is the amount of energy a sound wave carries per second through a unit area. The closer the sound wave is to its source, the more energy it has in a given area. As the sound wave moves away from the source, the wave spreads out and the intensity decreases.

INTERACTIVITY

Explore how the frequency and intensity of a sound wave affect the sound you hear through headphones.

Intensity of Sound

Figure 4 ✏ Sound waves spread out as they travel away from the source producing the sound. For each of the locations in the image, rank the intensity of the sound waves coming from the band on a scale of 1 to 3, with 1 being the greatest intensity.

VIDEO

GO ONLINE to access...
Teaching Video Students delve deeper into a lesson concept.

Loudness and Pitch

Address Misconceptions Students may have many misconceptions about sound. One common misconception is that hitting an object with more force changes its pitch. Demonstrate the lab where students plucked a guitar string and found that amplitude determines loudness. Have students listen carefully to see if pitch changes when the string is plucked more forcefully and with a greater amplitude. Students should hear that only the loudness changes.

Teach with Visuals Have students examine the figure Intensity of Sound. Ask: For a person in the audience, what two factors affect the intensity of sound they hear? (*how loud the band is and how far away the person is from the band*)

INTERACTIVITY

GO ONLINE to access...
Sound Students will explore which properties of a sound wave determine pitch and loudness in the context of evaluating how well headphones work.

DIFFERENTIATED INSTRUCTION

L3 Support Advanced Students
Have students model the compression and rarefaction of sound in air using a drawing. Ask: What would be the difference in the model or its movement for two sounds at different loudness? What happens to the model as the sound travels away from the source and gets less loud? How does this relate to the intensity of the sound?

LESSON 3

Academic Vocabulary

Activate Prior Knowledge Have students...

- read the sentence that uses the word *differentiate*.
- write words that are similar to *differentiate*. (*differ, different, differential*)
- choose the root word for *differentiate*. (*different*)
- explain what the root word (*different*) means. (*not the same*)
- identify the part of speech that *differentiate* has in the sentence. (*verb*)
- work out the meaning of *differentiate*. (*to identify the differences between things*)

Math Toolbox MP.2

Use Ratio Reasoning Guide students in using a logarithmic scale by having them...

- create a two-column chart in which the difference in decibels in intervals of 10 is placed in the left column and the corresponding amount by which a sound's power level is multiplied for that difference is placed in the right column.
- practice using the chart by completing the following frames:
  - When the amount of decibels increases by 20, a sound's power level increases by a factor of _____. (*100*)
  - When the amount of decibels decreases by 40, a sound's power level decreases by a factor of _____. (*10,000*)
  - A sound increased in power by a factor of 1,000 and reached a level of 60 decibels. The initial level was _____ decibels. (*30*)
  - A sound decreased in power by a factor of 10 and reached a level of 40 decibels. The initial level was _____ decibels. (*50*)

Academic Vocabulary

What is the root word in *differentiate*? How does this help you figure out the word's meaning?

The root word of differentiate is different. This helps me figure out that this word means we need to look at differences between things being compared.

Measuring Loudness So, how do our ears **differentiate** between a light knock and a hard knock on a door? Loudness can be measured by a unit called a **decibel** (dB). The greater the decibels of the sound, the louder that sound seems to a listener. The loudness of a sound you can barely hear, such as a pin dropping to the floor, is about 0 dB. When someone lightly taps on your door, the loudness is about 30 dB. But if someone pounds on your door, that loudness might increase to 80 dB! Sounds louder than 100 dB, such as the sound of a chainsaw, can cause damage to people's ears, especially if they are exposed to the sounds for long periods of time. Music technicians use equalizers to change the loudness levels of different frequencies of sound, as in **Figure 5**.

Using an Equalizer
Figure 5 You can use an equalizer to adjust the loudness of sound waves at different frequencies. Raising the decibel level of low frequencies increases the bass tones of music. How might you increase the high-pitched tones of music?
Increase the decibel level of higher frequencies.

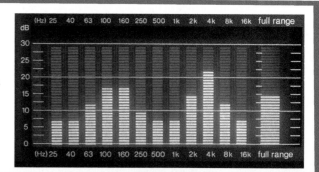

Math Toolbox
Decibel Levels

Every 10-decibel increase represents a tenfold increase in intensity and power. For example, when loudness increases from 20 to 30 decibels, a sound's power is multiplied by 10. If loudness increases by 10 again, power increases by another factor of 10. Therefore, when loudness increases from 20 to 40 decibels, power increases by a factor of 100!

1. **Use Ratio Reasoning** If a sound's power level increases from 20 decibels to 50 decibels, by what factor does its power increase?
   10 × 10 × 10 = 1,000, power is multiplied by 1,000

2. **Reason Quantitatively** If you want to lower the loudness of the bass tones in your music by 20 decibels, by how much does the intensity need to decrease?
   It must decrease by a factor of 100.

PROFESSIONAL DEVELOPMENT

Develop Classroom Collaboration

There are many different kinds of instruments. Plan a class discussion on how different instruments produce sound, including the human voice. Ask students to be prepared to discuss specific instruments they know about or to demonstrate instruments they bring from home. Have students discuss the relative pitch and loudness of different instruments.

Thickness Affects Pitch

Figure 6 On a standard 6-string guitar, the strings range in thickness.

✏ On the photo, draw an X on the guitar string that has the lowest pitch.

Factors Affecting Pitch Have you ever heard someone describe a note on a piano as "high-pitched" or "low-pitched"? The **pitch** of a sound refers to how high or low the sound seems. Pitch depends upon the frequency of the sound waves. Sound waves with a high frequency have a high pitch, and waves with a low frequency have a low pitch.

The frequency of a sound wave depends upon how fast the source of the sound is vibrating. For example, when people speak or sing, the air from their lungs moves past their vocal cords and makes the cords vibrate, producing sound waves. When vocal cords vibrate more quickly, they produce higher-frequency sound waves with higher pitches. When vocal cords vibrate more slowly, they produce lower-frequency sound waves with lower pitches.

This phenomenon happens with all things that vibrate and produce sound waves. Guitars produce sound when someone strums or plucks their strings. If you've ever studied a guitar, then you may have noticed that its strings vary in thickness. The thicker strings of a guitar vibrate more slowly than the thinner strings do, and so the thicker strings have a lower frequency, and therefore a lower pitch, than the thinner strings (**Figure 6**).

Teach with Visuals Have students examine the figure Thickness Affects Pitch. Ask:

- How does the thickness of the string vary from top to bottom? *(The strings change from thickest at the top to thinnest at the bottom.)*
- Which vibrates faster, a thicker string or a thinner string? *(a thinner string)*
- Why will a thinner string vibrate faster? *(A thinner string has less mass and will accelerate faster when the same force is applied to it.)*
- Which has lower pitch when vibrating, a thicker string or a thinner string? *(a thicker string)*

SCAFFOLDED QUESTIONS

Use the questions below to assess students' depth of understanding of the content on this page. Have students support their responses with evidence from the text.

Identify Pitch refers to which property of sound? *(how high or low the sound is)* **DOK 1**

Fill In A sound that has a higher frequency also has a higher _____. *(pitch)* **DOK 1**

Explain Wind instruments make sound by vibrating air inside the tube. When the pitch becomes higher, what changes? *(the air vibrates faster)* **DOK 2**

DIFFERENTIATED INSTRUCTION

L1 Support Struggling Students
Have students pair up and discuss the question "What do you know about pitch?" Then have pairs complete one of the following assignments to better understand low and high pitch: create drawings or symbols to illustrate low and high pitch; write examples and non-examples of low and high pitch; write definitions of high and low pitch.

L3 Support Advanced Students
People can hear sound in the range of 20 Hz to 20,000 Hz. Other animals can hear sound at different ranges. Whales and dolphins can hear the largest range of sound, from 70 Hz to 150,000 Hz. Whales and dolphins are also better than people at determining the direction of the source of sound. Have students propose reasons why these animals have such good hearing.

LESSON 3

The Doppler Effect

Literacy Connection RST.6-8.7

Integrate With Visuals Have students meet in groups and draw the sound waves surrounding the motorcycle. Then have students answer the following questions:

- What do the sound waves look like? (*Depictions should show circles closer together in the direction the motorcycle is moving toward and farther apart in the direction the motorcycle is moving away from.*)
- The time interval between waves passing is the frequency. What is the relationship between the spacing of the lines of the circles and frequency? (*The closer together the lines are, the higher the frequency.*)
- Where is the driver of the motorcycle in relationship to the sound waves that are being generated? (*The driver is always inside the innermost circle.*)

INTERACTIVITY

GO ONLINE to access...
Doppler Effect Students observe the Doppler effect and analyze how stationary sources of noise compare to moving sources of noise.

What it is A video followed by two flipbooks and short-answer assessment gadgets

What it does The interactivity enables the student to consider how the compression and extension of waves changes what they sound like.

How to use it Review wave interactions. Then have students recall a time they heard an emergency vehicle pass Ask how the sound of the siren changed as the vehicle approached and as it drove away.

NEXT GENERATION SCIENCE STANDARDS

MS-PS4-2 Develop and use a model to describe that waves are reflected, absorbed, or transmitted through various materials.

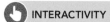

INTERACTIVITY

Explain how sounds from moving objects can change in pitch.

Literacy Connection

Integrate With Visuals
Do you think the motorcyclist would hear a change in pitch of the motorcycle's sound as he passes by you? Why or why not?

He would not. He is traveling with the sound waves, so he does not observe the change in frequency.

The Doppler Effect

Have you ever had a loud motorcycle drive by you and heard the pitch of the engine noise change? Change in pitch occurs because the movement of the source of the sound causes a sound wave to either compress or stretch. As the motorcycle approaches, the peaks of the emitted sound waves are scrunched together. When the peaks are closer together, the sound waves have a higher frequency. As the motorcycle moves away, the peaks of the emitted sound waves are spread out. The sound waves then have a lower frequency.

A change in frequency is perceived by a listener as a change in pitch. This change in frequency (and therefore, in pitch) of the sound wave in relation to an observer is called the **Doppler effect. Figure 7** shows the Doppler effect when a firetruck rushes by a person on the sidewalk.

✓ **READING CHECK** **Summarize** What property of a sound wave determines the pitch of a sound?

frequency

The Doppler Effect
Figure 7 As a firetruck speeds by, an observer detects changes in the pitch of the truck's siren. The firetruck approaches the observer in the first image. It then passes her and continues on.
CCC Cause and Effect ✏
Draw the sound waves as the truck moves away.

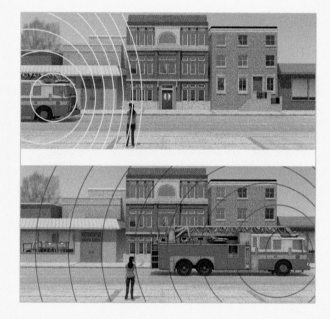

PROFESSIONAL DEVELOPMENT

Reflect
What misconception did students have about sound?

How could a common misconception be addressed in the lesson?

☑ LESSON 3 Check

1. Identify What is the cause of any sound wave?

A sound wave is caused by a vibration.

2. SEP Construct Explanations Explain why sound waves are mechanical waves rather than electromagnetic waves.

Sound waves are mechanical because they require a medium to travel through.

3. SEP Communicate Information Why does sound travel more quickly through a solid than through a liquid or a gas?

Sample: Sound waves travel quickest through most solids because they are less compressible than liquids or gases.

4. Form a Hypothesis Dogs can hear higher-pitched whistles that humans do. How do you think the sound frequencies that dogs can hear compare to the frequencies that humans can hear?

Dogs can hear frequencies above the range of human hearing, since higher pitches mean higher sound wave frequencies.

5. CCC Cause and Effect What effect might spending years working on a construction site have on a person's hearing? Why?

The person's hearing may be damaged, because construction sites produce sounds at high decibel levels that can cause harm to the human ear after long periods of exposure.

6. Apply Concepts Ultrasound, also known as sonography, is a technology that uses high-frequency sound waves to produce images. It is used in medical applications to help doctors see inside patients' bodies. How do you think the sound waves can be used to image bones, muscles, and other internal structures?

Sample: The sound waves reflect off different parts of the body, such as bones and organs, and are recorded back at the device that generates the ultrasounds. This allows the user to map out the interior of the body.

7. SEP Develop Models Imagine a person is sitting on a beach, and a speedboat passes by on the water. Draw a model of this situation, and indicate how the Doppler effect would influence how the sound waves coming from the boat would be perceived by the person on shore.

Sample model should show the sound waves closer together as the boat approaches the person and farther apart as the boat moves away. Student indicates that the sound would be higher-pitched as the boat approaches and lower-pitched as it moves away.

33

☑ LESSON 3 Check

 DOCUMENT

GO ONLINE to download...
L3 Enrichment Extend student understanding of the lesson. **Editable**

DEMONSTRATE

Assessment and Remediation

☑ **ASSESSMENT**

GO ONLINE to access...
Lesson Quiz Formally assess students' learning from the lesson using this auto-graded online assessment. **Editable**

 DOCUMENT

GO ONLINE to download...
L1 Remediation This auto-assigned remediation document provides targeted support for students who struggle on the assessment. **Editable**

Depth of Knowledge

DOK Level	Questions
1	1, 2
2	3, 4, 6
3	5, 7

Lesson Check Scoring Notes

Assess students' responses to short-answer question using the rubrics below:

4. Form a Hypothesis DOK 2,
2 points

2pt	Student explains that higher pitch corresponds to higher frequency.
2pt	Student explains that dogs can hear higher sound frequencies than humans.

7. SEP Develop Models DOK 3,
6 points

2pt	Student drawing shows circles (for sound waves) around boat.
2pt	Circles are closer together for approaching and farther apart for moving away.
2pt	Student relates higher pitch to approaching and lower pitch to moving away.

Electromagnetic Waves

OBJECTIVES

Students will identify
• the characteristics of electromagnetic waves.

Students will compare
• models of electromagnetic wave behavior.

Students will explore
• the waves that make up the electromagnetic spectrum.
• how models describe the way that frequency and amplitude are related in waves.

CONNECT
0.5 class period

📱 **APP** .... (15)
Vocabulary App

📄 **DOCUMENT** .... (10)
Class Discussion

LESSON 4 .... (20)
Student Edition

📖 **ETEXT** .... (20)

NEXT GENERATION SCIENCE STANDARDS

MS-PS4-2 Develop and use a model to describe that waves are reflected, absorbed, or transmitted through various materials.

DCI PS4.B Electromagnetic Radiation When light shines on an object, it is reflected, absorbed, or transmitted through the object, depending on the object's material and the frequency (color) of the light.

DCI PS4.B Electromagnetic Radiation The path that light travels can be traced as straight lines, except at surfaces between different transparent materials (e.g., air and water, air and glass) where the light path bends.

DCI PS4.B Electromagnetic Radiation A wave model of light is useful for explaining brightness, color, and the frequency-dependent bending of light at a surface between media.

DCI PS4.B Electromagnetic Radiation However, because light can travel through space, it cannot be a matter wave, like sound or water waves.

CCC.6 Structure and Function Structures can be designed to serve particular functions by taking into account properties of different materials, and how materials can be shaped and used.

SEP.2 Developing and Using Models Develop and/or use a model to predict and/or describe phenomena.

Model It!

Polarizing Glasses

SEP Develop Models These sunglasses allow light through only if the light waves are oriented vertically. Draw the light wave that passes through each lens.

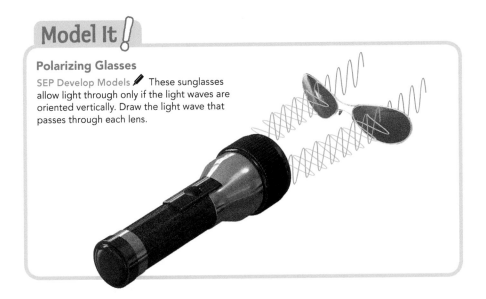

Particle Model of Light The wave model of light does not explain all of its properties. For example, when a beam of high-frequency light shines on some metals, it knocks some tiny particles called electrons out of the metal. This is called the photoelectric effect. However, lower-frequency light such as red light doesn't have enough energy to knock the electrons out.

The photoelectric effect can be explained by thinking of light as a stream of tiny packets, of energy instead of as a wave. Each packet of light energy is called a photon. For the effect to occur, each photon must contain enough energy to knock an electron free from the metal.

One property of light that the wave model explains but the particle model does not is diffraction. When light passes through a narrow enough slit, instead of forming one image of the slit on a screen, it spreads out and produces a striped pattern of light and dark areas. This is similar to a water wave passing through a narrow channel and then spreading out on the other side.

▶ **VIDEO**

Watch this video to compare the wave and particle models of light.

👆 **INTERACTIVITY**

Explore the particle model of light yourself.

✔ **READING CHECK** Summarize Light is described as what two things in the two models you just read about?

waves and a stream of particles

37

Model It! SEP Develop Models Have students model polarized light and the filters that can separate the waves.

• Encourage them to think about the different ways to depict the waves, e.g., the trough of one being where the crest of the other is found.

• Have students explain the importance of polarized filters as it relates to the types of waves found in the world around them. How are polarized filters useful?

▶ **VIDEO**

GO ONLINE to access...
Teaching Video Students delve deeper into a lesson concept.

👆 **INTERACTIVITY**

GO ONLINE to access...
Models of Light Using an online simulation, students experiment with light to simulate the particle model. They review the concepts of the particle model and the behavior of light while filling the role of optical engineer.

✔ **READING CHECK** WHST.6-8.2.f

Summarize Guide students in summarizing their observations in their notes.

• Have students review the main ideas of the content on the page.

• Guide students in including the main ideas and a few clarifying details when they write their notes.

DIFFERENTIATED INSTRUCTION

L1 Support Struggling Students

Some students may have difficulty with the idea that light can behave both as a wave and as a particle. To help them visualize these concepts, ask them to imagine a stream of tiny particles flowing as if in a river. Next, have them imagine that stream behaving as if it were a wave itself, rising and falling with different frequencies.

L3 Support Advanced Students

Have students research some of the uses of the photoelectric effect. Next, ask them to explain how the photoelectric effect works as best as they can using terms from this topic.

INVESTIGATE

Wavelength and Frequency

Teach With Visuals After students have completed and labeled the diagram in **Wavelengths and Frequencies**, check for understanding by asking them to add labels for the location of microwaves (between radio waves and visible light), ultraviolet (between visible light and X-rays), and gamma rays (beyond X-rays). Ask them to describe the wavelengths, frequencies, and energy of each of the additional types of electromagnetic radiation in comparison to the ones that are on the diagram.

✓ READING CHECK

Draw Conclusions Have students draw connections between what they have already learned and the relationship between wavelength and energy.

- Review the visual depictions of the different waves and point out their varying wavelengths.
- Guide students in explaining the connection between frequency and energy.
- Have students identify which wave has the highest frequency.

Assess on the Spot To prepare for the next section of the material, have students present an exit ticket with as many types of electromagnetic waves as they can remember.

Literacy Connection
Translate Information
How is visible light similar to and different from radio waves?

Both are electromagnetic
waves, but radio waves
have much longer wave-
lengths, shorter frequen-
cies, and lower energies
than visible light.

Wavelength and Frequency

If you use a wave model for electromagnetic waves, the waves have all of the properties that mechanical waves do. Namely, each wave has a certain amplitude, frequency, wavelength, wave speed, and energy. Electromagnetic waves are divided into categories based on their wavelengths (or frequencies). Visible light, radio waves, and X-rays are three examples of electromagnetic waves. But each has properties that make it more useful for some purposes than for others. If you tried to microwave your food with radio waves, or make a phone call with X-rays, you wouldn't get very far! All electromagnetic waves travel at the same speed in a vacuum, but they have different wavelengths and different frequencies.

As you can see in **Figure 3**, wavelength and frequency are related. In order for a wave to have a high frequency, its wavelength must be short. Waves with the shortest wavelengths have the highest frequencies. Frequency is also related to energy. Higher frequency waves have more energy, while lower frequency waves have less energy.

Visible light is the only range of wavelengths your eyes can see. A radio detects radio waves, which have much longer wavelengths than visible light. X-rays, on the other hand, have much shorter wavelengths than visible light.

Wavelengths and Frequencies

Figure 3 🖊 Use the information from the text to label the three wavelength ranges shown in the diagram as either X-rays, radio waves, or visible light.

✓ **READING CHECK** **Draw Conclusions** Of X-rays, radio waves, and visible light, which wave type has the most energy? Explain.
X-rays, because they have the highest frequencies

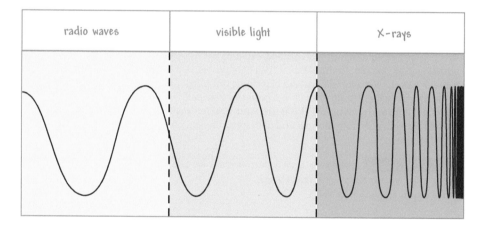

| radio waves | visible light | X-rays |

PROFESSIONAL DEVELOPMENT

Develop Classroom Collaboration

When teaching some concepts that cannot be easily observed in the macroscopic world, such as the particle model of light, some students may gain understanding in a variety of ways, including sketching and using models. Allow students to collaborate in groups and explore wave behavior using items such as online simulators and spring toys. The observations of one student's choices might inform another student's understanding of the concepts.

The Electromagnetic Spectrum

There are many different types of electromagnetic waves. The complete range of electromagnetic waves placed in order of increasing frequency is called the **electromagnetic spectrum**. The electromagnetic spectrum is made up of radio waves, microwaves, infrared rays, visible light, ultraviolet rays, X-rays, and gamma rays. The full spectrum is shown in the Math Toolbox.

Radio Waves Electromagnetic waves with the longest wavelengths and the lowest frequencies are **radio waves**. Radio waves are used in mobile phones. Towers, such as the one in **Figure 4**, receive and transmit radio waves along a network that connects mobile phones to each other, to the Internet, and to other networks.

Mobile Phones
Figure 4 Mobile phones depend on a network of towers to transmit, receive, and relay radio signals.

Math Toolbox

Frequencies and Wavelengths of Light

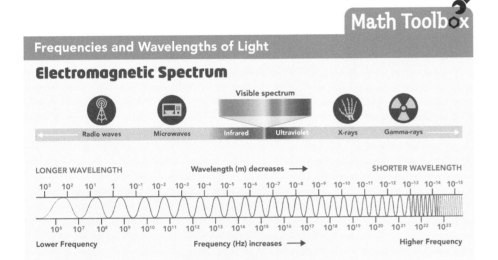

Use the electromagnetic spectrum to answer the following questions.

1. Draw Comparative Inferences Which has a higher frequency: microwaves or blue light? How do you know?

   Blue light; energy increases as you move right on the diagram. Visible light, which includes blue light, is to the right of microwaves on the diagram.

2. SEP Use Models If a certain electromagnetic wave has a wavelength of 100 m, what type of electromagnetic wave is it? How do you know?

   Radio waves; according to the scale on the diagram, 10^2 is in the radio wave portion of the diagram on the far left.

The Electromagnetic Spectrum

College and Career Readiness

X-ray technicians are crucial members of many medical science teams. Their ability to help safely and accurately image parts of bodies can help doctors diagnose and treat many different conditions. Most work side-by-side with doctors to treat patients.

Math Toolbox  MP.2

Draw Comparative Inferences Guide students as they complete the math activity.

- Direct students to look at the graphic showing the electromagnetic spectrum. As a class, identify which end of the spectrum has the highest energy and which has the lowest energy.
- Have students identify where the two frequency values would fall on the spectrum.

DIFFERENTIATED INSTRUCTION

L1 Support Struggling Students

Support students in understanding the electromagnetic spectrum by presenting them with a blank diagram of the spectrum with places for them to label the frequency and wavelength on a scale from low to high and from short to long.

L3 Support Advanced Students

Draw an example wavelength spectrum on the board. Describe three types of electromagnetic waves to advanced students and have them place labels on the spectrum depending on where they think the types of waves are located. As an additional challenge, have them classify the correct range for each type of wave.

LESSON 4

Connect to the Real World: Lasers and Medicine Electromagnetic radiation has many different frequencies and wavelengths. The high energy of high-frequency radiation could come in useful in some unexpected ways. Students are likely familiar with lasers from movies and television shows, but they are probably less familiar with the use of lasers for such health purposes as optical surgery (LASIK) and laser therapy to help improve acne scars and skin health. If class time allows, discuss these topics with students to strengthen the real-world connection.

HANDS-ON LAB

 GO ONLINE to download...

⨕Investigate

Build a Wave In this lab, students develop and use a model to describe the basic properties of a wave. Next, they use a mathematical representation to connect these properties with specific types of waves, such as electromagnetic waves or sound waves. **Editable**

Class Time ⏱ 40

Group Size groups

Materials (per group) paper, metric ruler, scissors, tape, glue, general materials for models (e.g., wire, rope, string, cardboard, dryer hose, spring toys, pipe insulators, dry macaroni, toothpicks, popsicle sticks, wood)

Procedure Tips Look over students' sketches for their models before they begin constructing them. Show students possible materials for their three-dimensional model. Encourage them to look for other items they can use. Discuss with students an appropriate size range for the wave properties that they will use in their models.

Lighting Up the Radar Gun

Figure 5 Radar guns are used in law enforcement to stop speeding drivers, but they are also used to measure the speeds of pitches in a game of baseball. Some pitchers' fastballs have been clocked at 105 miles per hour!

HANDS-ON LAB

⨕**Investigate** Develop a model of a wave.

Microwaves Microwaves have shorter wavelengths and higher frequencies than radio waves. When you think about microwaves, you probably think of microwave ovens. But microwaves have many other uses, including radar. Radar is a system that uses reflected microwaves to detect objects and measure their distance and speed. Radar guns, such as the one in **Figure 5**, are used to measure the speed of a baseball pitch. Police also use them to detect cars that are traveling over the speed limit.

Infrared Rays If you turn on an electric stove's burner, you can feel it warm up before the heating element starts to glow. The invisible heat you feel is infrared radiation, or infrared rays. **Infrared rays** are electromagnetic waves with wavelengths shorter than those of microwaves. An infrared camera uses infrared rays instead of visible light to take pictures called thermograms, such as the one in **Figure 6.**

Visible Light Electromagnetic waves that you can see are called **visible light**. Visible light waves have shorter wavelengths and higher frequencies than infrared rays.

Recall that light waves bend, or refract, when they enter a new medium, such as water or glass. Light from the sun contains electromagnetic waves of many frequencies, both visible and invisible. Sunlight passing through a prism splits into its different frequencies, forming a rainbow pattern. After rainy conditions, rainbows such as the one in **Figure 7** can also form in the sky.

Thermogram

Figure 6 ✏ Label the blank spaces rectangles on the thermogram with temperatures in degrees Celsius.

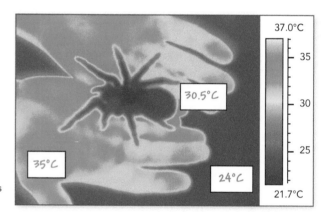

PROFESSIONAL DEVELOPMENT

Reflect

Which types of electromagnetic radiation were students most familiar with?

....

....

Did their prior knowledge of some types of electromagnetic radiation seem to help their grasp of the concept, or did they bring misconceptions along with prior knowledge? How can their misconceptions be addressed?

....

....

Color Filters Perhaps you have looked at an object that has a colored light shining on it. You might have noticed that the color of the object looks different than it does when white light shines on it. The color of the light might come from white light shining through a colored filter—a tinted piece of glass or plastic. A red filter, for example, transmits only red light. When light shines through a red filter onto an object, any part of the object that is red, looks red. Any other color looks black. **Figure 3** shows several different color filters and what happens when white light shines on them.

Color filters are often used in photography and movies. They are part of the special effects that create different moods for scenes. Use what you know about filters to complete the activity in **Figure 3**.

Literacy Connection

Evaluate Media Describe an image you've seen with a filter on it, and write about how the filter altered the image.

Sample: A friend posted a photo of the ocean and used a blue filter to make it appear brighter blue.

Photography and Color Filters

Figure 3 🖊 Color filters can be used in photography to bring out certain colors or create dramatic moods. For each of the inset images, write the color of the filter that produced the altered images.

red

green

47

DIFFERENTIATED INSTRUCTION

L1 Support Struggling Students
Have students draw a red object, a blue object, and a green object. Explain that this is the color of the objects in white light. Guide students to make a drawing showing the color of the three objects when red light shines on them, when blue light shines on them, and when green light shines on them. Ask students to explain the pattern they see.

L3 Support Advanced Students
Have students research and write a report on why the sky appears blue most of the day but can appear other colors in the morning or evening.

Address Misconceptions Students may have many misconceptions about light. One misconception is that the color of an object is not affected by the illuminating light. Students may believe that the true color of an object is seen in white light and that when colored light illuminates a colored object, the color of the light mixes with the color of the object. Have students describe their ideas about the color of an object in colored light before and after completing the interactivity.

SCAFFOLDED QUESTIONS

Use the questions below to assess students' depth of understanding of the content on this page. Have students support their responses with evidence from the text.

Recite What determines the color of an object? *(The color that is reflected from it.)* **DOK 1**

Describe How do colored light filters work? *(They transmit only part of white light, the part that is the color of the filter.)* **DOK 2**

Describe An object is blue in white light. The object is then placed in green light. Does the object transmit, absorb, or reflect the green light? *(The object absorbs the green light.)* **DOK 2**

Explain An object is blue in white light. The object is then placed in green light. What color does the object appear? Explain. *(The object appears black because it absorbs all the green light falling on it. No light is reflected, and objects that don't reflect light appear black.)* **DOK 3**

LESSON 5

Reflecting Light

Assess on the Spot Have students pair up and write down three things they learned about mirrors from the text. Record students' answers. *(smooth surface, regular reflection of light, rays of light reflect at the same angle, creates an image)*

HANDS-ON LAB

📄 **GO ONLINE to download...**

и**Investigate**

Light Interacting With Matter Students use different models to observe and describe how light waves can interact with various materials. **Editable**

Class Time 55

Group Size (groups)

Materials (per group) white paper cup, flashlight, metal can, plane mirror, convex mirror, concave mirror, pencil, transparent plastic or glass cup, water, cardboard box, white paper, tape, prism

Procedure Tips
- All parts: Check students' data tables.
- Parts B and C: Warn students to be careful of any sharp edges or broken mirror pieces.
- Part D: The shift in the pencil may be easier to observe if the pencil is placed toward the back of the cup.
- Part E: Do activity on a sunny day. Caution students not to look directly at the sun. Tell them to stand with their backs to the sun and hold the box and prism high enough so that the sunlight shines over their shoulders into the prism.
- Part E: For best results, the spectrum should appear in a shadowed part of the box.
- Part E: Tell students to observe and record the order of the colors in the spectrum.

HANDS-ON LAB

и**Investigate** Discover how light is reflected, refracted, and transmitted.

Reflecting Light

You have seen that sometimes light is transmitted through materials. Like other electromagnetic radiation, light can also be reflected. The reflection of light occurs when parallel rays of light bounce off a surface. Reflected light is how you see your image in a mirror, but reflected light is also why you see a distorted image or no image at all in the surface of rippling water on a lake. The difference lies in whether the light undergoes regular reflection or diffuse reflection.

Regular reflection occurs when parallel rays of light hit a smooth surface. As shown in **Figure 4**, the trees are reflected because light hits the smooth surface of the water, and the rays all reflect at the same angle. As a result, the reflection is a clear image.

In **diffuse reflection**, parallel rays of light hit an uneven surface. The angle at which each ray hits the surface equals the angle at which it reflects. The rays, however, don't bounce off in the same direction because the light rays hit different parts of the surface at different angles. **Figure 4** shows why light undergoes diffuse reflection when it hits choppy water on a lake.

Regular and Diffuse Reflection

Figure 4 Light reflects off the surface of water.
✏️ For each type of reflection, circle the terms that correctly complete the sentence.

You (can / cannot) see an image in the still water because the light undergoes (regular / diffuse) reflection.

You (can / cannot) see an image in the choppy water because the light undergoes (regular / diffuse) reflection.

PROFESSIONAL DEVELOPMENT

Beyond the Content

Light behaves both as a particle and as a wave. In 2015, scientist were able to observe this duality for the first time. Scientists at the Ecole Polytechnique Fédérale de Lausanne in France designed a clever experiment in which they shot laser light waves and electrons along a very small metal wire. The laser waves traveled in both directions along the wire and created a standing wave that radiated light around the wire when they met. Then, electrons were also shot along the wire and were used to produce an image of the standing wave with an ultrafast electron microscope. The microscope also showed electrons slowing down and speeding up as they encountered the standing wave. This occurs because of an energy exchange between the electrons and light particles (photons).

Mirror Images

The most common way to form a clear image using reflected light is with a mirror. There are three different types of mirrors—plane, convex, and concave. The types of mirrors are distinguished by the shape of the surface of the mirror.

The mirror you have hanging on a wall in your home probably is a flat mirror, also known as a plane mirror. The image you see in the mirror is called a virtual image, which is an image that forms where light seems to come from. **Figure 5** shows an example of a virtual image in a plane mirror. This image is upright and the same size as the object that formed the image, but the right and left sides of the image are reversed.

Convex Mirrors

To visualize a convex mirror, think about a metal bowl. A **convex** mirror is like the outside of the bowl because it is a mirror with a surface that curves outward. If you look at an image in the outside of the bowl, it is smaller than the image in a plane mirror. **Figure 6** shows an example of an image in a convex mirror. To understand how these images form, look at the optical axis and the focal point of the mirror. The optical axis is an imaginary line that divides a mirror in half. The **focal point** is the location at which rays parallel to the optical axis reflect and meet. The light reflects off the curved surface such that the image appears to come from a focal point behind the mirror.

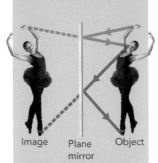

Image   Plane   Object
         mirror

Plane Mirror Image
Figure 5 In this virtual image, the reflected light rays appear to come from behind the mirror, where the image forms. The distance from the image to the mirror is the same as the distance from the object to the mirror.

Convex Mirror Image
Figure 6 Most rear-view mirrors are convex. Light rays bend when they hit the surface of the mirror in such a way that the object appears smaller than it is.

Optical axis

Focal point

49

LESSON 5

☑ READING CHECK RST.6-8.4

Classify Have students examine the pictures and text in the figure **Mirror Images** to help them answer the question.

Focus on Mastery!

Model It! SEP Develop Models Have students work in groups to determine what kind of mirror will make a door look smaller and rounder. Have students answer the following questions to help them complete this task:

- How does the size of an image reflected in a convex mirror compare to the size of the object? *(It looks smaller.)*
- How does the size of an image reflected in a concave mirror compare to the size of the object? *(It looks smaller or larger, depending on the relative position of the object and the focal point.)*
- When does a concave mirror create an image that looks smaller than the object? *(If the object is farther from the mirror than the focal point is, an inverted real image is created that looks smaller than the object.)*
- When does a concave mirror create an image that looks larger than the object? *(If the object is closer to the mirror than the focal point is, a real image is created that looks larger than the object.)*

Assess on the Spot Have students write down how a real image is different from a virtual image. *(A real image is inverted.)*

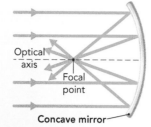

Optical axis

Focal point

Concave mirror

Mirror Images
Figure 7 The images formed by mirrors depend upon the shape of the mirror. Examine the diagram, and then identify the type of image in each example.

The object is located farther from the mirror than the focal point is. It forms a ___real___ image.

The object is located between the mirror and the focal point. It forms a ___virtual___ image.

Concave Mirrors Just as a convex mirror is like the outside of a shiny bowl, a concave mirror is like the inside of the bowl. The surface of a **concave** mirror curves inward. **Figure 7** shows that the focal point of a concave mirror is on the reflecting side of the mirror. The image that forms from a concave mirror depends on whether the object is between the focal point and the mirror or farther away from the mirror than the focal point. If the object is farther from the mirror than the focal point is, then reflected light rays cross past one another, and the image is inverted. This image is called a real image. If the object is between the focal point and the mirror, then the image is not inverted and is larger than the actual object. This image is a virtual image.

☑ READING CHECK Classify If a mirrored image is inverted, what type of image is it?

___real___

Model It

Fun with Mirrors
In a fun house, mirrors are often used to change the appearance of objects.

SEP Develop Models ✎ Suppose you want to use a mirror to make a door look smaller and rounder. In the space below, draw the mirror and the door, along with the focal point. Label the mirror with the type of mirror it is.

Student models should include a convex mirror and a door in front of it. The door's reflection in the mirror should appear smaller than the door itself. The mirror should be labeled "convex."

PROFESSIONAL DEVELOPMENT

Beyond the Content

The human eye focuses light in a number of steps to produce sharp images. What is this process? Light enters the eye through the cornea, which refracts light due to its shape—convex—and to the differences in refraction indices between it and air. Light then moves through the pupil, the size of which is controlled by muscles in the iris, and into the lens. The curvature of the lens stays unchanged when looking at objects in the distance. When we look at objects close by, the ciliary muscles tighten to make the lens bulge and become more convex. Light then travels into the vitreous humor, the transparent jellylike tissue filling the eyeball behind the lens. Refraction occurs here due to differences in refraction indices. The real image created is projected on the retina, the layer of light-sensitive cells at the back of the eyeball. Nerve impulses travel from the retina to the brain, where a visual image is formed.

Lenses

Light not only reflects, as it does with a mirror, but it also bends, or refracts. A lens is a curved piece of transparent material that refracts light. Every time you look through a telescope, a microscope, or a pair of eyeglasses, you are looking through a lens. Just like a mirror, a lens is either convex or concave, based on its shape.

Convex Lenses Look at **Figure 8** to see what convex lenses look like, how they refract light, and what type of image is produced. You can see that convex lenses are thicker in the middle and thinner at the edges. As light passes through the lens, it refracts toward the center of the lens. The more curved the lens is, the more the light refracts.

A convex lens can produce either a virtual image or a real image depending on where the object is located relative to the focal point of the lens. If the object is between the lens and the focal point, then a virtual image forms. This image is larger than the actual object. You may have observed this when using a magnifying glass. If the object is farther away from the lens than the focal point is, then a real image forms. This image can be larger, smaller, or the same size as the object.

Does this description of a convex lens sound familiar? **Compare** a convex lens and a concave mirror. Both a convex lens and a concave mirror focus light, and the type of image formed depends on the location of the object compared to the location of the focal point.

VIDEO

Explore the effects of different lenses and filters in cameras.

Academic Vocabulary

How does comparing items differ from contrasting them?

Comparing is observing how things are alike, and contrasting is observing how they are different.

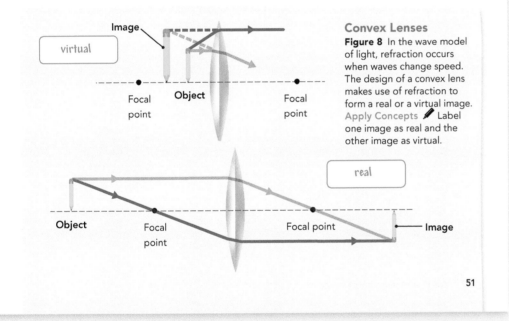

virtual

Image

Focal point

Object

Focal point

Convex Lenses

Figure 8 In the wave model of light, refraction occurs when waves change speed. The design of a convex lens makes use of refraction to form a real or a virtual image. Apply Concepts ✏ Label one image as real and the other image as virtual.

real

Object

Focal point

Focal point

Image

51

Academic Vocabulary

Activate Prior Knowledge Help students understand the terms *compare* and *contrast* by…

• reviewing the etymology of *compare* and *contrast*. *Compare* contains the Latin root *compar*, which means "like, equal." *Contrast* contains the Latin root *contra*, which means "against."

• having students define the terms in their own words and discussing their definitions with a partner.

 VIDEO

GO ONLINE to access…
Teaching Video Students delve deeper into a lesson concept.

SCAFFOLDED QUESTIONS

Use the questions below to assess students' depth of understanding of the content on this page. Have students support their responses with evidence from the text.

Fill In A lens is made of a _____ material. *(transparent)* **DOK 1**

Recite How does light behave when it travels through a lens? *(It bends, or refracts.)* **DOK 1**

Explain What determines what kind of image is formed when light is refracted through a convex lens? *(Position of the object; if the object is between the lens and the focal point, then a virtual image forms; if the object is farther away from the lens than the focal point, then a real image forms.)* **DOK 2**

DIFFERENTIATED INSTRUCTION

L1 Support Struggling Students

Have students label diagrams in which parallel rays of light reflect from a convex mirror and a concave mirror (these diagrams can be made by advanced students). Have students label *object, convex mirror, concave mirror, optical axis, focal point, virtual image,* and *real image.*

L3 Support Advanced Students

Have students create diagrams in which parallel rays of light reflect from a convex mirror and a concave mirror. Have students include the creation of a virtual image and a real image with a concave mirror.

LESSON 5

READING CHECK RST6-8.7

Compare and Contrast Have students scan the text and underline...

• the kind of material a mirror is made from.
• how light is focused by a mirror.
• what kind of images are formed with a concave mirror.
• the kind of material a lens is made from.
• how light is focused by a lens.
• what kind of images are formed with a convex lens.

SYNTHESIZE

INTERACTIVITY

GO ONLINE to access...
Predicting the Behavior of Light
Rays Students describe the behaviors of light being reflected and explain how these behaviors apply to everyday objects such as cell phone screens.

What it is A multimedia introduction to the concept followed by multiple-choice and short-answer on-the-spot assessments

What it does The interactivity enables students to make connections to the real world regarding wave behaviors.

How to use it Ask students to brainstorm types of reflective surfaces and consider why different materials have different reflective properties.

DOCUMENT

GO ONLINE to download...
L3 Enrichment Extend student understanding of the lesson. **Editable**

NEXT GENERATION SCIENCE STANDARDS

MS-PS4-2 Develop and use a model to describe that waves are reflected, absorbed, or transmitted through various materials.

INTERACTIVITY

Predict the behavior of light rays as they encounter different objects and substances.

Concave Lenses Concave lenses are thinner at the center than they are at the edges. When light rays travel through the lens, the rays are bent away from the optical axis, so the rays never meet. Because the rays never meet, concave lenses form only virtual images, and these images are upright and smaller than the objects. **Figure 9** shows how concave lenses form images.

READING CHECK **Compare and Contrast** In what ways is a convex lens like a concave mirror? In what ways are they different?
Both concave mirrors and convex lenses focus light, and the type of image formed depends on the location of the object compared to the location of the focal point. A mirror reflects light, while a lens refracts it.

Concave Lenses
Figure 9 When looking through a concave lens, a virtual image forms which is always smaller than the object itself.
Apply Concepts ✏ After examining the diagrams, circle the photo in which the image is formed by using a concave lens.

Object   Focal point   Image   Focal point

Focal point   Object   Image   Focal point

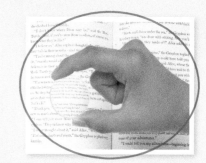

PROFESSIONAL DEVELOPMENT

Reflect
Which activities helped students develop a model of how light behaves?

How did you help students distinguish between the different kinds of mirrors and lenses?

✓ LESSON 5 Check

1. Classify What kind of material transmits some light, making objects behind it appear blurry?

translucent material, such as waxed paper

2. Identify A bird runs into the window of a building because it sees the reflection of the sky in the window. The sky does not appear distorted in this window. What type of mirror or lens is the window acting as? Explain your answer.

It is like a plane mirror because light rays are reflected in the same direction they strike the window.

3. SEP Design Solutions When a person is nearsighted, an eyeglass lens is needed to bend light entering the eye away from the optical axis. What type of lens will do this?

a concave lens

4. CCC Cause and Effect Why might some rear-view mirrors in a car state, "Objects are closer than they appear"?

Convex mirrors are used, and because the image is smaller, the objects seem farther away.

5. SEP Construct Explanations Suppose a movie director is filming on a set that should look like a hot desert. He wants the scene to appear warmer, such that the red and yellow tones are the most apparent. What color filters should he use? What color will the blue sky appear when he uses those filters, and why?

He should use red and yellow filters since they will transmit red and yellow light which will make the scene appear warmer. The blue sky will appear black since it does not reflect red or yellow light.

Quest CHECK-IN

In this lesson, you observed how light behaves when it encounters transparent, translucent, and opaque objects. You saw how the color of light or filters affects the color of objects. You also discovered the ways that light can reflect from mirrors or refract through lenses.

CCC Structure and Function How might you apply this knowledge to choose the objects and their placement in your quest?

I can think about the barrier that light must get around, and how I can use the behavior of light. For instance, since light reflects from mirrors, I can use mirrors to reflect light around the barrier and lenses to refract the light as needed.

HANDS-ON LAB

An Optimal Optical Solution

Go online to download the lab worksheet. Build and test your optical security system.

53

✓ LESSON 5 Check

Quest CHECK-IN

HANDS-ON LAB

📄 **GO ONLINE to access...**
An Optimal Optical Solution Students design and test an optical security system. **Editable**

DEMONSTRATE

Assessment and Remediation

✓ ASSESSMENT

GO ONLINE to access...
Lesson Quiz Formally assess students' learning from the lesson using this auto-graded online assessment. **Editable**

📄 DOCUMENT

GO ONLINE to download...
L1 Remediation This auto-assigned remediation document provides targeted support for students who struggle on the assessment. **Editable**

Lesson Check Scoring Notes

Assess students' responses to short-answer question using the rubrics below:

4. CCC Cause and Effect DOK 3, 4 points

2pt	Student explains that the image seen in a convex mirror appears smaller than the object would normally look at that distance.
2pt	Student explains that because the object appears smaller, it also appears farther away and this is why the warning is placed on some rearview mirrors.

5. SEP Construct Explanations DOK 3, 4 points

2pt	Student explains that using red and yellow filters will cause these colors to be reflected. (Student may note green is also reflected by the red filter.)
2pt	Student explains that the sky will appear black if red and yellow filters are used because there is no blue light to be reflected.

Depth of Knowledge

DOK Level	Questions
1	1, 2
2	3
3	4, 5

53

TOPIC 1

Assessment and Remediation

Error Analysis

Use the Review and Assess questions on this page as a formative assessment. Implement the targeted feedback strategies and reference the short answer rubrics to determine additional student support needed prior to the summative Topic Test.

3. Correct answer: A. Sound travels faster through water than air. **DOK 2** If a student chose...
- B, first ask student how sound waves travel (*a vibrating object pushes particles of matter, which push other particles of matter*) and then ask which kind of matter has particles more closely packed together, water or air? (*water*) More closely packed particles transmit sound waves faster.
- C or D, ask student how sound waves travel (*through matter*) and if there is matter in space to transmit sound waves (*There is not*).

NEXT GENERATION SCIENCE STANDARDS

MS-PS4-1 Use mathematical representations to describe a simple model for waves that includes how the amplitude of a wave is related to the energy in a wave.

MS-PS4-2 Develop and use a model to describe that waves are reflected, absorbed, or transmitted through various materials.

☑ # TOPIC 1 Review and Assess

① Wave Properties

MS-PS4-1

1. Which of the following is a property of a mechanical wave?
Ⓐ amplitude   B. weight
C. incidence   D. color

2. The sound wave frequency of an F-sharp in music is 370 Hz, and its wavelength is 0.93 m. What is the wave's speed?
A. 34.4 m/s   B. 397.9 m/s
Ⓒ 344.1 m/s   D. 300,000 km/s

3. Which statement about the speed of sound is correct?
Ⓐ Sound travels faster through water than air.
B. Sound travels at the same speed through water and air.
C. Sound travels faster through space than air.
D. Sound travels at the same speed through space and air.

4. If the amplitude or frequency of a wave increases, the energy of the wave ....*increases*....

5. **SEP Construct Explanations** It's been said that you can estimate how far away a lightning bolt is by counting the number of seconds that elapse between seeing the flash and hearing the thunderclap, and then dividing that number by five to get a distance in miles. In terms of the physics of light and sound waves, does this method make sense?
Yes. Generally, we see lightning as soon as it occurs, as long as we are relatively close to it. But sound moves more slowly—about one-fifth mile per second. So if we count seconds after seeing lightning, we are measuring how far the thunder is traveling by fifths of a mile.

② Wave Interactions

MS-PS4-2

6. Refraction is the bending of waves that occurs due to a change in
Ⓐ speed.   B. frequency.
C. height.   D. amplitude.

7. Which of the following pairs of terms describes the two different wave interactions depicted below?

 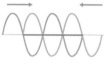

Ⓐ constructive and destructive interference
B. moving and standing waves
C. mechanical and electromagnetic waves
D. sound waves and light waves

8. When a ray of light strikes a surface, it can be ....*reflected*...., ...*refracted*...., or ....*absorbed*....

9. **SEP Engage in Argument** Why is it important for engineers to understand the natural frequency of vibrations in building materials when planning to build a bridge in an area with high winds or frequent earthquakes?
If vibrations added by wind or earthquake tremors happen to match the natural frequency of vibrations in the building's structural materials, the waves passing through the building will increase in amplitude, and destruction is more likely to occur.

---

5. **SEP Construct Explanations DOK 3,** 4 points

2pt	Student explains how the counting method works.
2pt	Student explains why the method makes sense.

7. Correct answer: A. The first diagram depicts constructive interference; the second depicts destructive. **DOK 3** If a student chose...
- B, ask student to compare these diagrams to the diagram of standing waves in Lesson 2.
- C, ask student to compare these diagrams to the diagram of an electromagnetic wave in Lesson 3.
- D, remind student that sound waves are longitudinal waves and have student review the model of a longitudinal wave in Lesson 1.

3 Sound Waves

MS-PS4-2

10. When a sound wave is absorbed by an object,
A. it quickly gains energy.
B. it quickly loses energy.
C. it slowly gains energy.
D. its energy does not change.

11. CCC Cause and Effect How do stiffness, density, and temperature affect sound waves?

Sample: A sound wave travels faster through a stiffer material. A sound wave will also travel faster through a denser material. A sound wave will move through a warmer object faster than a cooler one.

4 Electromagnetic Waves

MS-PS4-2

12. Which electromagnetic wave type has the highest frequency?
A. visible light
B. infrared rays
C. gamma rays
D. microwaves

13. Of all of the colors in the visible part of the electromagnetic spectrum, red light has the lowest frequency, the ......highest...... wavelength, and the ......lowest...... energy.

14. SEP Use Models Describe how you could use a simple rope to teach someone about the different waves along the electromagnetic spectrum.

I would tie the rope to a door and wiggle the rope up and down to model a transverse wave. I would then use this model to explain the concepts of wavelength, frequency, and amplitude.

5 Electromagnetic Radiation

MS-PS4-2

15. Which statement is correct?
A. A red apple reflects green light.
B. A blue ball absorbs blue light.
C. A green leaf reflects green light.
D. A black shirt reflects all colors of light.

16. What happens when light rays encounter a concave lens?
A. The light rays are reflected back.
B. The light rays travel through the lens and refract away from the center of the lens.
C. The light rays travel through the lens and refract toward the center of the lens.
D. The light rays travel through the lens without bending.

17. When an object is located between a concave mirror and the focal point, a ......virtual...... image is produced.

18. SEP Develop Models ✏ Draw a model to show what happens to light when it meets a convex mirror.

Students should draw a convex mirror with light rays striking it. The light rays should reflect off the surface and bend outward.

55

11. CCC Cause and Effect DOK 2, 4 points

3pt	Student explains that sound waves travel faster through stiffer, denser, and warmer materials.
1pt	Student summarizes information using scientific vocabulary.

12. Correct answer: C. Gamma rays have the highest frequency of wave on the electromagnetic spectrum. **DOK 2**
If a student chose...
• A or B, have student review which wavelengths of electromagnetic waves are visible to humans.
• D, remind student that microwaves do not go through materials due to the lower frequency.

14. SEP Use Models DOK 3, 4 points

2pt	Student explains how rope can be used to simulate the behavior of waves.
2pt	Student correctly identifies the different types of waves along the electromagnetic spectrum.

16. Correct answer: B. Light rays travel through the lens and refract away from the center of the lens. **DOK 2**
If a student chose...
• A, have student list materials that reflect light.
• C, model how this result occurs when light interacts with a convex lens.
• D, show student a pair of eye glasses. Hold the glasses a short distance from the text to model how light bends as it interacts with curved lenses.

18. SEP Develop Models DOK 3, 5 points

2pt	Student illustrates light interacting with a convex mirror.
3pt	Student illustrates light reflecting outward from a convex mirror.

9. SEP Engage in Argument DOK 3, 4 points

2pt	Student identifies the importance of vibrations.
2pt	Student answer involves the concept of resonance.

10. Correct answer: B. As sound waves reach an object, they lose energy quickly. **DOK 2**
If a student chose...
• A or C, demonstrate how sound changes by ringing an alarm in the air and then placing a box over the alarm as it rings. The sound will be much quieter because the sound waves lose energy when they interact with the box.
• D, remind student that all sound waves eventually lose energy, otherwise sounds would continue indefinitely.

Depth of Knowledge

DOK Level	Questions
1	1, 4, 6, 7, 12, 17
2	2, 3, 8, 10, 11, 13, 15, 16
3	5, 9, 14, 18

Spark a Debate Review the criteria Bianca's design needs to meet. You may want to do this by asking different students to read each criterion. Then have students…

- study the illustration of Bianca's design on their own and find a material they think needs to change to better meet the criteria.
- write down their change and an explanation of why the original material didn't meet the criteria.
- meet with three other peers and present an argument for their change; students should debate if they disagree.
- work with their peers to complete a final list of changes to materials that will help Bianca's design better meet the criteria.

Focus on Mastery!

SEP Develop Models Guide students in modeling how sound travels from the speaker by asking them to…

- draw a sketch of where the speaker is in the auditorium. Tell students to use the whole page to make the sketch.
- represent sound waves traveling from the speaker with concentric circles. Explain that only part of each circle is inside the auditorium. If compasses are available, students can use them to draw the circles.
- gradually decrease the width of the lines of the circles from the innermost circle to the outermost circle, to represent the decrease in amplitude and intensity that occurs when sound waves travel farther from the source.
- identify where the sound is the loudest and where it is most quiet using their model.

NEXT GENERATION SCIENCE STANDARDS

MS-PS4-1 Use mathematical representations to describe a simple model for waves that includes how the amplitude of a wave is related to the energy in a wave.

MS-PS4-2 Develop and use a model to describe that waves are reflected, absorbed, or transmitted through various materials.

☑ TOPIC 1 Review and Assess

MS-PS4-1, MS-PS4-2

Evidence-Based Assessment

Bianca is helping the theater director at her school with lighting, sound, and set design for a school play. She will be choosing the materials that will be used on stage and on the walls of the theater. After she reads the script and makes observations inside the theater, she makes the following list of the factors to consider in her design.

- The echoes throughout the theater need to be reduced.
- The set should not reflect too much light into the audience's eyes.
- The only lights available are white, purple, and yellow. The filters available are red and blue.
- The blue sky on the set should appear black for Act 2.

Bianca draws a detailed illustration of her plan to show the theater director. She labels it with the materials she plans to use.

PROFESSIONAL DEVELOPMENT

Reflect

Which teaching strategies that you used throughout this topic best promoted students' understanding?

....

....

....

....

1. **Apply Scientific Reasoning** Bianca plans to shine a few spotlights on the sky for Act 2 and use a filter to change the color. Which filter should Bianca use on the white light to make the blue sky appear black?
   - (A) a red filter
   - B. a blue filter
   - C. a white filter
   - D. no filter at all

2. **Identify Criteria** Which of the following considerations does Bianca need to take into account as she works on the set and lighting design? Select all that apply.
   - ☐ Two different sets are needed for Act 2.
   - ☑ The set materials should not be too shiny or glossy.
   - ☐ Only the colors white, purple, and yellow can be used to paint the sets.
   - ☑ The walls have hard surfaces that reflect sound waves.
   - ☐ Only the white lights can be used for Act 2.

3. **SEP Use Models** Based on Bianca's illustration, did she choose the appropriate material on the walls for reducing echoes? Why or why not?
   Yes. She chose felt, which is a soft material that will absorb sound waves. So there will be fewer echoes throughout the theater.

4. **SEP Develop Models** As sound waves travel away from the speaker, their amplitudes and energy decrease. Where will the sound be the most quiet? If you were to move the speaker, where would you place it and why?
   As it is right now, the sound will be quietest at the back corner of the theater opposite to the speaker. I would move the speaker to the floor in front of the center of the stage so that one side of the room is not louder than the other.

5. **SEP Design Solutions** Based on Bianca's criteria and model, which materials would you change on stage? Explain your reasoning.
   Sample: Aluminum would be shiny and reflect light into the audience's eyes. It might also reflect sound and cause echoes. I would use wood for the walls of the castle and paint them gray instead.

Complete the Quest!

Phenomenon Reflect on your demonstration and answer questions about modifying and improving your design. List some other kinds of jobs that may require a good knowledge of light and its behavior.

Apply Concepts You've seen how light can bend and move. How might a grocery store manager use the properties of light and set up objects to make sure the entire store can be visible from one location without using cameras?

The manager could use mirrors all around the store. The light would reflect off the mirrors to an observer at one location.

👆 **INTERACTIVITY**

Reflect on Your Demonstration

57

DIFFERENTIATED INSTRUCTION

L1 Support Struggling Students
Assign each student a criterion from the assessment prompt to review. Have student write a solution that meets that criterion. Then have students meet in pairs and carry out peer review of their work.

L3 Support Advanced Students
Have students scan the unit and identify and annotate text that provides information to address each criterion.

Scoring Notes

Use the grading rubrics to assess students' responses to short-answer questions.

3. SEP Use Models DOK 2, 4 points

2pt	Student explains that a material that absorbs sound will reduce echoes.
2pt	Student identifies the material on the walls and correctly notes if it absorbs sound.

4. SEP Develop Models DOK 3, 6 points

2pt	Student identifies the corner farthest from the speaker as the place where the sound is most quiet.
2pt	Student identifies the center of the stage as a better place for the speaker.
2pt	Student explains that moving the speaker will ensure that the loudness of the sound is more even on both sides of the auditorium.

5. SEP Design Solutions DOK 3, 4 points

2pt	Student identifies aluminum as a material that does not meet the criteria because it reflects light and sound.
2pt	Student proposes alternative materials to aluminum that are not reflective.

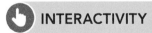

👆 **INTERACTIVITY**

GO ONLINE to access...
Reflect on Your Demonstration Students synthesize their learning from the Quest activities and lessons by putting together their Findings and answering reflection questions. Through their Findings, students demonstrate their ability to engage in argument from evidence.

uDemonstrate Lab

Performance-Based Assessment

Use this lab as a Performance-Based Assessment to assess students' mastery of the standards. In addition to disciplinary core ideas, this lab allows students to demonstrate the science and engineering practices of interpreting data and engaging in argument from evidence.

Investigative Phenomenon Students apply the phenomena of water waves interacting with solid barriers and with other water waves to identify the best method of diminishing these waves.

Purpose

In this lab, students will experiment by creating different types of waves and exploring their characteristics. By altering the properties of waves with the use of force, lenses, and more, students can see waves in action and observe their properties as a direct result of their choices.

Class Time (40)

Group Size groups

Materials Notes
📄 **GO ONLINE to download**
the master materials list, which also identifies kit materials.

NEXT GENERATION SCIENCE STANDARDS

MS-PS4-2 Develop and use a model to describe that waves are reflected, absorbed, or transmitted through various materials.

---

uDemonstrate Lab

MS-PS4-2

Making Waves

How can you use a **model** to demonstrate what happens when **waves interact** with barriers or other waves?

➤ Background

Phenomenon A wave breaker is a large wall made of rocks or concrete objects that extends into the ocean. Breakers often are built near beaches to make the water calmer for swimmers. These barriers help to diminish the force of incoming waves by scattering them and interfering with their movements.

In this lab, you will model the behavior of water waves and explain how the waves interact with each other and with objects in their paths. You will then decide on the best method and materials for diminishing waves.

Materials

(per group)
- water
- plastic dropper
- metric ruler
- paper towels
- modeling clay
- plastic knife
- cork or other small floating object
- ripple tank (aluminum foil lasagna pan with mirror on the bottom)

Safety

Be sure to follow all safety guidelines provided by your teacher.

This rock barrier helps to block big waves and make the beach more enjoyable for swimmers.

PROFESSIONAL DEVELOPMENT

Collaborate with Colleagues

Some of the best investigations come from novel and unexpected findings. Discuss this lab with your colleagues and consider other ways in which you can alter and enhance this experiment to better illustrate the nature of waves. Some examples might include the use of items such as food coloring or larger pans of water.

Design an Investigation

HANDS-ON LAB
Demonstrate Go online for a downloadable worksheet of this lab.

☐ One way to generate waves is to squeeze drops of water from an eyedropper into a pan of water. How can you use the dropper to control how forceful the waves are?

Sample: The more forceful I squeeze the water out of the dropper, the more forceful the waves will be, and vice versa.

☐ What questions will you explore in your investigation? Some questions to explore include:

- What happens when waves hit a solid surface?
- What happens when waves travel through a gap between two solid objects?
- How does a floating object react to waves?
- What happens when one wave meets another wave?

☐ Record any additional questions you hope to answer in your investigation.

Student questions will vary.

☐ Design an experiment to show how waves behave when they interact with different objects or with each other. Write out a procedure. Then decide what information to record and design a data table to record your observations.

59

DIFFERENTIATED INSTRUCTION

L1 Support Struggling Students

Have students first identify a characteristic of waves that they wish to explore and then think of as many ways as they can to investigate. For example, exploring the effect of speed on waves can lead them to creating waves first quickly and then slowly in the water.

L3 Support Advanced Students

Have students devise their own experiments exploring the effect of two types of influences on a wave. For example, they might explore the effect of both speed and medium on frequency.

Safety
Spills should be wiped up as quickly as possible.

Advanced Prep
Gather the listed materials. You might want to fill the trays with water and place them at lab benches prior to the beginning of class.

HANDS-ON LAB

📄 **GO ONLINE to download...**
this lab and additional teacher support.
Editable

Procedure Tips

- If your students need more direction on this lab, use the sample procedure to guide their work.
- If students are investigating the reflection of waves off a solid surface, tell them to look at the water near the surface. The reflected waves may be small and weak and easy to overlook.
- Observing interference in a water tank can be difficult. The best results can be seen if students make regularly spaced waves from two synchronized point sources. Such waves can be produced by repeatedly dipping the ends of pipe cleaner bent in a wide U shape into the water tank.
- In general, students will have to experiment with different methods of making and observing waves to investigate various wave interactions.

HANDS-ON LAB

📄 **GO ONLINE to download...**
Do-It-Yourself Inquiry Use this version to challenge advanced students to plan more of the investigation on their own. **Editable**

uDemonstrate Lab

DOCUMENT

GO ONLINE to download...
Performance-Based Assessment Use this rubric to assess students' levels of mastery of the standards based on their work on this lab.
Editable

Expected Outcomes

When a cork is added to each situation described below, the cork will bob up and down slightly but remain nearly in the same place in the pan.

- **Pan side** Wave bounces back in a circular pattern from end of pan.
- **Paper towel on side** Wave does not bounce much from side with towel.
- **Clay in center of tank** Waves bounce from clay and go around the ends.
- **Clay at angle in tank** Waves bounce at an angle of incidence from clay.
- **Opening with two pieces of clay** Waves go through opening and spread out.
- **Opening with two pieces of clay at an angle** Wave goes through opening, with some of it bouncing off the side.
- **Clay with three gaps** A wave comes through each opening and spreads out after leaving the opening.

uDemonstrate Lab

Procedure

1. I took a deep aluminum pan and added approximately 1 1/2 to 2 inches of water and placed a mirror on the bottom.

2. I used the dropper to dispense one drop of water into the pan and observed. I did this several times trying to change the force by which the drops were released from the dropper.

3. I added a cork to the center of the water and observed as I created waves.

4. I created a solid wall out of the clay and placed it across the center of the pan. I created waves and observed the water in both sides of the pan.

5. I used the knife to cut a section of the clay out to create a gap in the wall. Again, I created waves and observed the water in both sides of the pan.

Data

Students' data tables should clearly organize their data and observations. For each interaction they investigate, students should record detailed observations on how the waves behaved.

PROFESSIONAL DEVELOPMENT

Reflect

During which parts of the lab were students best able to demonstrate their understanding?

....

....

What did you learn by completing this lab with students?

....

....

Analyze and Interpret Data

1. Identify Are the waves in water mechanical waves or electromagnetic waves? How do you know?

They are mechanical waves. Electromagnetic waves are waves of light. These waves are mechanical energy that move through a medium—water.

2. CCC Cause and Effect In what situations did you observe waves interfering with one another? How did it affect the amplitude of the waves?

When I use the dropper in two places, I saw the waves interfere. Depending on where I used the dropper, sometimes the waves would interfere and become a larger wave. Sometimes they would interfere and become a smaller wave.

3. Claim Which material and set-up was best for reducing waves? Which was worst?

Sample: A clay wall with no gaps was best. Cork floats and diminishes waves the least.

4. Evidence What evidence led you to your conclusions?

The clay was the heaviest and stopped waves from passing through. Cork did not stop waves from passing through it.

5. Reasoning Repetition is when you repeat a step of the procedure a few times to see if you get the same results. Did you use repetition in your experiment? Why or why not?

Sample: Yes; I observed how waves would hit a clay barrier twice to see if I obtained the same results.

6. SEP Design Solutions Share your results with members of another group. What did they do differently? In what ways would you suggest that the other group members revise their procedure?

Sample: They did not use the paper towel. They should have tried using the paper towel as a barrier to see if it stops waves better than clay.

61

3. Claim DOK 3, 3 points

2pt	Student identifies a best and a worst material.
1pt	Student describes evidence on which they based their decision.

6. SEP Design Solutions DOK 3, 2 points

1pt	Student identifies the ways in which the procedures of the groups differed.
1pt	Student suggests appropriate and scientifically sound revisions.

DIFFERENTIATED INSTRUCTION

Touch base with individual students as they are working on the Analyze and Interpret Data questions. You can also download this lab and edit the wording of the questions following these suggestions.

L1 Support Struggling Students

Restate Question 4: What is different about the behavior of waves in your model and the behavior of waves in a harbor? Students should be able to explain that the model is much smaller than the real thing and does not include factors such as people and sand that would affect the waves.

L3 Support Advanced Students

Encourage students to extend their thinking beyond the questions on the page. Ask: How could you improve your model to depict more accurately what happens in an isolated harbor? A busy tourist town?

TOPIC 2 OVERVIEW

Information Technologies

STORYLINE	SELECT TOPIC RESOURCES	
TOPIC LAUNCH		
This topic introduces students to information signals and the technologies that encode and transmit that information. Students study digital and analog signals in order to compare their advantages and disadvantages.	▶ **VIDEO** Professional Development .... ⏱5 ☑ **ASSESSMENT** Topic Readiness Test .... ⏱15 📄 **DOCUMENT** **L1** Topic Remediation Summary ...... ⏱15	⚗ **иConnect** Lab .... ⏱20 **Essential Question** .... ⏱5 ▶ **VIDEO** *Quest* KICKOFF ⏱15
LESSON 1 Electric Circuits		
Students identify the three components of electric circuits and describe relationships among voltage, current, and resistance. Students model series and parallel circuits.	⚗ **иInvestigate** Lab .... ⏱15 HANDS-ON LAB *Quest* CHECK-IN .... ⏱40 👆 **INTERACTIVITY** иEngineer It! STEM ⏱15	**Engineering Design Notebook** .... ⏱70 📄 **DOCUMENTS** **L1** Remediation .... ⏱15 **L3** Enrichment .... ⏱15
LESSON 2 Signals		
Students describe the possible ways that information signals can be sent and model the encoding of information into analog and digital signals.	⚗ **иInvestigate** Lab .... ⏱20 Case Study .... ⏱30 👆 **INTERACTIVITY** *Quest* CHECK-IN ...... ⏱10	📄 **DOCUMENTS** **L1** Remediation .... ⏱15 **L3** Enrichment .... ⏱15

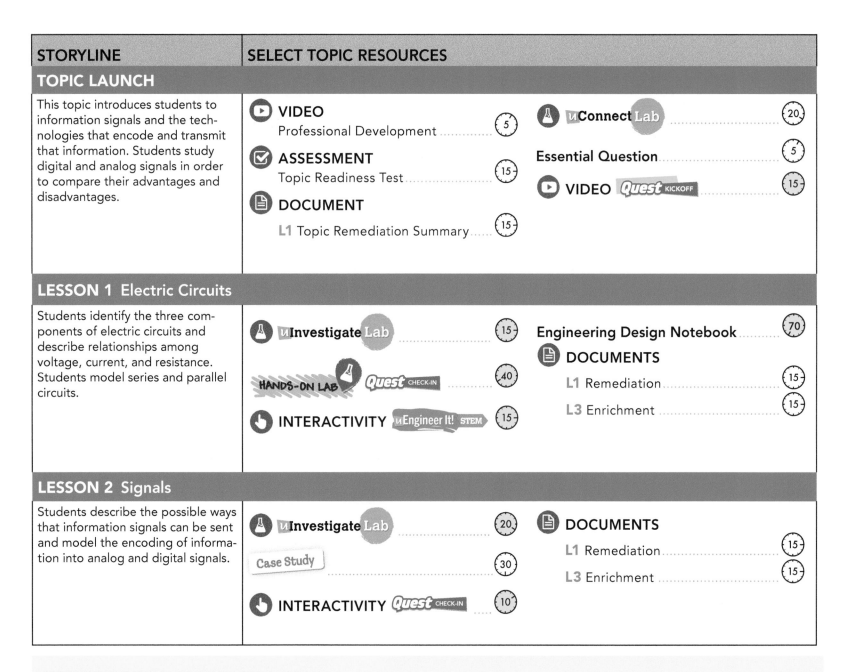

NEXT GENERATION SCIENCE STANDARDS

MS-PS4-3 Integrate qualitative scientific and technical information to support the claim that digitized signals are a more reliable way to encode and transmit information than analog signals.

STORYLINE	SELECT TOPIC RESOURCES

LESSON 3 Communication and Technology

Students describe different kinds of communications technologies and model the transmission of analog and digital signals in order to compare their reliability and security.

🧪 **uInvestigate Lab** .... (30)

EXTRAORDINARY SCIENCE .... (15)

▶ **VIDEO**
Career Video .... (5)

📱 **VIRTUAL LAB** .... (20)

👆 **INTERACTIVITY** *Quest* CHECK-IN (40)

📄 **DOCUMENTS**
L1 Remediation .... (15)
L3 Enrichment .... (15)

TOPIC CLOSE

As students learn that digital signals are more reliable and secure than analog signals, they apply their new knowledge and improved practices to model the encoding, sending, receiving, and decoding of both kinds of signals.

TOPIC 2 Review and Assess .... (30)

☑ **ASSESSMENT**
Topic Test .... (40)

👆 **INTERACTIVITY**
L1 Topic Remediation .... (10)

👆 **INTERACTIVITY** *Quest* FINDINGS (20)

🧪 **uDemonstrate Lab** .... (30)

SHORT ON TIME?
🕐 Use these assets with the yellow clock.

DIFFERENTIATED INSTRUCTION
L1 Struggling Students **L3** Advanced Students

Information Technologies

Use the grade-band endpoints identified below to help you prioritize instruction and integrate the dimensions.
MS-PS4-3

	Grades 3–5 **Students should already be capable of . . .**	Grades 6–8 **Students are working toward . . .**
SCIENCE AND ENGINEERING PRACTICES		integrating qualitative scientific and technical information in written text with that contained in other media.
SEP.8 Obtaining, Evaluating, and Communicating Information	combining information in written text with that contained in corresponding tables or graphs.	
		recognizing that a simple wave has a repeating pattern with a specific wavelength, frequency, and amplitude.
DISCIPLINARY CORE IDEAS		
PS4.A Wave Properties	understanding that waves are regular patterns of motion.	recognizing that multiple technologies are based on the understanding of waves and how they interact with matter.
PS4.C Information Technologies and Instrumentation	understanding that patterns can encode, send, receive, and decode information.	
		using graphs and charts to identify patterns in data.
CROSSCUTTING CONCEPTS		
CCC.1 Patterns	recognizing that patterns can be used to describe natural phenomena.	recognizing that the properties of a material influence how that material can be shaped and used.
CCC.6 Structure and Function	understanding that different materials have different substructures.	

Grades 9–12
Students will develop the skills of . . .

comparing and evaluating sources of information presented in different media or formats.

understanding that wavelength and frequency are related to one another by a wave's speed of travel.

understanding that very large amounts of information can be stored and transported after being digitized.

analyzing and interpreting patterns to improve the design of a system.

examining the properties of different materials when investigating processes or systems.

College & Careers
As adults, students can apply these skills by . . .

using text and visual displays to simulate systems and interactions.

using knowledge of wave properties to understand tools of digital communication.

pursuing a career as a software developer, analyzing users' needs and creating applications in response.

TOPIC 2
Information Technologies

Using Phenomena Students observe a circuit board and then ask questions about how it can reliably transmit information.

HANDS-ON LAB

📄 **GO ONLINE to download...**

иInvestigate

Continuous or Discrete? Students determine whether given scenarios involve continuous data or discrete data.

Class Time 20

Group Size pairs

Materials (per pair) graph paper

Procedure Tips Monitor student discussion during the activity. As needed, ask guiding questions such as:

• Does the number of volunteers need to be a whole number, or could it be a fraction or decimal? *(a whole number)*

• What does this tell you about whether the data set is continuous or discrete? *(The graph of the data will be a set of unconnected points with whole number x-values, so the data set is discrete.)*

NEXT GENERATION SCIENCE STANDARDS

MS-PS4-3 Integrate qualitative scientific and technical information to support the claim that digitized signals are a more reliable way to encode and transmit information than analog signals.

LESSON 1
Electric Circuits
u**Investigate Lab:** Electric Current and Voltage

u**Engineer It!** STEM **A Life-Saving Mistake**

LESSON 2
Signals
u**Investigate Lab:** Constructing a Simple Computer Circuit

LESSON 3
Communication and Technology
u**Investigate Lab:** Let the Music Play

NGSS PERFORMANCE EXPECTATIONS
MS-PS4-3 Integrate qualitative scientific and technical information to support the claim that digitized signals are a more reliable way to encode and transmit information than analog signals.

What do these tiny circuits do?

HANDS-ON LAB

u**Connect** Consider ways to represent the terms *continuous* and *discrete*.

Topic Materials List

📄 **GO ONLINE to download a detailed, editable master materials list.**

Consumables
• poster board
• tape
• graph paper

Nonconsumables
• D-cell batteries in battery holders
• 3-V light bulbs in sockets
• 1.5-V light bulbs in sockets
• 30-cm lengths of insulated wire

• alligator clips
• no. 2 pencils
• carbon grains
• plastic cups
• copper strips
• single pole-single throw knife switches
• double pole-single throw knife switches
• pegboards
• machine screws
• vinyl record

• hand lens
• microscope
• needle
• large spring coil
• 9-volt or type C batteries
• electrical switches

GO ONLINE
to access your
digital course

- ▶ VIDEO
- 👆 INTERACTIVITY
- 🧪 VIRTUAL LAB
- ☑ ASSESSMENT
- 📖 eTEXT
- ⚗ HANDS-ON LABS

The Essential Question

Why are digital signals a reliable way to produce, store, and transmit information?

SEP Construct Explanations Circuit boards are found in all kinds of electronics devices, from toasters to televisions. How is information transmitted through these boards?

Sample: Information is transmitted through these devices in the form of electric currents.

63

DIFFERENTIATED INSTRUCTION

L1 Support Struggling Students

Have students describe what kinds of information are sent by cell phones. Explain that a cell phone converts information into digital signals and transmits them to another cell phone. The other cell phone converts the digital signals back into the original form of information.

L3 Support Advanced Students

Help students distinguish between the form of a signal and the coding of a signal. Explain that the form of a signal can be electronic, which is current, or in electromagnetic waves. Next, explain that the coding of a signal into digital or analog is not based on its form.

Focus on Mastery!

Using Phenomena Give students a minute to observe the details of the circuit board in the image. Then give students another minute to write down any questions they have about how information is reliably transmitted through the circuit board. Have students share their questions with the class. Discuss with students:

What do these tiny circuits do?

 The Essential Question

Activate Prior Knowledge

SEP Construct Explanations Explain that digital signals are the signals transmitted through circuits in digital devices such as computers, tablets, and cell phones. As a warm-up activity, have students pair up and describe...

- the different kinds of digital devices they use.
- the different ways that digital signals can be transmitted and stored.
- the different kinds of information that can be encoded into digital signals.
- what the word *reliable* means in terms of information.

Read the Essential Question to the class. Ask: What kind of information about digital signals do we need to know in order to determine if they are reliable?

As students continue through the topic, refer back to this essential question, and review how digital signals are created, transmitted, and stored.

Assessment and Remediation

 ASSESSMENT

GO ONLINE to access...
Use the auto-graded online assessment to determine whether your students are prepared for success in the upcoming topic. **Editable**

📄 **DOCUMENT**

GO ONLINE to download...
L1 Remediation Summary Support struggling students by providing additional preparation before beginning the topic. **Editable**

Quest KICKOFF

▶ VIDEO

GO ONLINE to access...

Testing, Testing... 1, 2, 3 Students watch a 5-minute video about how sound engineers record sound and identify the differences in audio devices from the past and the present. Students choose a specific scenario about recording sound and respond to question prompts that get them thinking about the goals of the recording and the challenges they might face.

STEM **Connect to the Real World: Music Recording** Students may not be aware of how much time and effort goes into the 3-minute song they're listening to. Making and recording a song is a collaboration among songwriters, musicians, sound technicians, and music producers. Each person has his or her own expertise. Songwriters and musicians have musical training. Engineers and sound technicians have the training to set up and operate the recording equipment. Music producers work on effects, arrangements, tempos, and which instruments to use. After much preparation, a song is ready to be recorded in a recording studio. A studio has specialized equipment such as microphones, effects boxes, sound mixing boards, and amplifiers. Students who may be interested in working in music recording can go online to explore college programs that offer degrees in music recording and music production.

NEXT GENERATION SCIENCE STANDARDS

MS-PS4-3 Integrate qualitative scientific and technical information to support the claim that digitized signals are a more reliable way to encode and transmit information than analog signals.

Quest KICKOFF

What is the best way to record sound for my scenario?

■ NBC LEARN ▶ VIDEO

STEM **Phenomenon** Sound engineers work on all kinds of audio recordings, from television shows and movies to music albums. If you wanted to record people's voices and manipulate them to use as sound effects, then how would you do it? In this Quest activity, you will identify the most reliable way to encode and transmit an audio recording. You will explore differences between analog and digital technologies with a hands-on lab and digital activities. By applying what you have learned, you will create a multimedia display that communicates your findings.

After watching the video, which looks at how an audio engineer records sound, describe how attending a live concert is different than listening to an album recorded in a studio.

At a live concert, musicians make mistakes and you hear audience noise. A studio album is edited and mixed to remove all mistakes and flaws.

👆 **INTERACTIVITY**

Testing, Testing . . . 1, 2, 3

MS-PS4-3 Integrate qualitative scientific and technical information to support the claim that digitized signals are a more reliable way to encode and transmit information than analog signals.

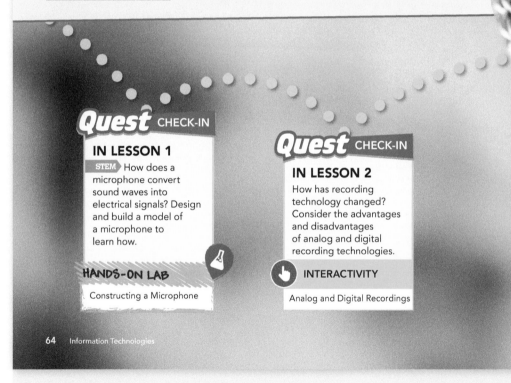

Quest CHECK-IN

IN LESSON 1

STEM How does a microphone convert sound waves into electrical signals? Design and build a model of a microphone to learn how.

HANDS-ON LAB

Constructing a Microphone

Quest CHECK-IN

IN LESSON 2

How has recording technology changed? Consider the advantages and disadvantages of analog and digital recording technologies.

👆 **INTERACTIVITY**

Analog and Digital Recordings

PROFESSIONAL DEVELOPMENT

Beyond the Content

A digital microphone has a sensor that converts analog audio sound waves directly into digital electronic signals. Digital microphones are found in a wide range of devices. There is a huge market for digital microphones in cell phones. Digital microphones are also found in computers, tablets, and video recorders. Headset microphones are used for specific applications. High-quality digital microphones are available for recording music and podcasts and for professional voice recording.

Microphones are just one of the many kinds of technology used to record sound.

Using Phenomena Start students thinking about the different technologies used to record and play back sound, such as different kinds of microphones, movies, TV, computers, cell phones, CDs, tapes, and vinyl records. Have students meet in small groups and discuss any differences in sound among different kinds of devices that play back music. Have students then discuss how they can ensure that they are recording the sound they want and not any of the sounds that they don't want.

Quest CHECK-IN

IN LESSON 3

What type of recording technology would best suit your scenario? Design a multimedia presentation that communicates your choices and reasons.

 INTERACTIVITY

Evaluate Recording Technologies

Quest FINDINGS

Complete the Quest!

Reflect on your work and identify fields or careers that require knowledge of analog and digital signals.

 INTERACTIVITY

Reflect on Your Recording Method

65

DOCUMENT

GO ONLINE to access...
Quest Checklist Students monitor their own progress as they complete the steps leading up to the Quest Findings. **Editable**

DOCUMENT

GO ONLINE to access...
Quest Rubric Assess students on their ability to identify criteria and constraints, implement the engineering design process, and communicate their final design.

Encourage peer revision and self-reflection as students use the grading rubric to review a draft of their Findings before turning in their final versions **Editable.**

DIFFERENTIATED INSTRUCTION

L1 Support Struggling Students
Create a template for the different parts of the multimedia display that students will make about the technology they will use for recording sound in their scenario. Guide students to fill in the template throughout the unit.

L3 Support Advanced Students
Some students may choose their own scenario and want to create an actual recording. Locate a mentor who can help these students extend the Quest.

uConnect Lab

Investigative Phenomenon Encourage students to think about when they have heard the words discrete and continuous. Have students synthesize their observations to form working definitions of continuous and discrete data.

Purpose

Students determine whether given scenarios involve continuous or discrete data.

Class Time 30

Group Size Pairs

This activity works best in pairs, where students are most likely to be actively engaged.

GO ONLINE to download...
the master materials list, which also identifies kit materials.

---

uConnect Lab

Continuous or Discrete?

Background

Phenomenon Scientists use data to identify patterns and make predictions. Some data is considered to be continuous, while other data is considered to be discrete. In this lab, you will investigate how you can determine whether data is continuous or discrete.

 How can you **use patterns** to distinguish between continuous and discrete data?

Materials

(per pair)
• graph paper

Safety

Be sure to follow all safety procedures provided by your teacher. The Safety Appendix of your textbook provides more details about the safety icons.

Design a Procedure

☐ 1. Consider these four scenarios.

  a. A botanist is studying plant growth. She measures the height of a tree each year for 10 years.

  b. An astronomer records the number of stars in the sky on one particular night that fit into each category: giant stars, white dwarfs, supergiant stars.

  c. A scientist records the temperature of a glass of hot water for 60 minutes as it cools down in a classroom.

  d. A geneticist records the number of people in a classroom that have one of the following genetic traits: brown hair, blue eyes, curly hair, left-handedness. *(note: the geneticist records the number of people for each separate trait)*.

☐ 2. **SEP Plan an Investigation** Develop a plan for how you can use these four scenarios to determine if a data set is continuous or discrete.

  ....

  ....

  ....

  ....

☐ 3. Show your plan to a teacher before you begin. Record your observations.

SAMPLE PROCEDURE

If your students need more direction on this lab, use the following procedure to guide their work.

Read each scenarios. Sketch a graph to model each situation. Think about whether each data set should be be a continuous line or a set of discrete points.

A. A botanist measures the height of a tree each year for 10 years.

  x = number of years
  y = height of the tree in meters

B. An astronomer records the number of stars in the sky on one particular night that fit into each category: giant stars, white dwarfs, supergiant stars.

  x = star categories (giant stars, white dwarfs, supergiant stars)
  y = number of stars

Observations

HANDS-ON LAB

Connect Go online for a downloadable worksheet of this lab.

Analyze and Interpret Data

1. CCC Patterns Based on your observations, what patterns did you notice between the data sets?

   Sample: I noticed that some data sets include data that can be counted, such as, the number of stars or the number of students. Other data sets include data that can be measured, such as, the height of a tree or the temperature of water.

2. SEP Construct Arguments For which scenarios was the data continuous? For which scenarios was the data discrete? Use evidence to support your argument.

   Sample: Scenario A involves continuous data. Scenario B involves discrete data. Scenario C involves continuous data, and Scenario D involves discrete data. In Scenario B, the stars can be counted. Similarly, in Scenario D, the geneticist is counting the number of students that have a specific trait, so the data values are all discrete. The other scenarios, which involve growth or temperature, represent continuous values.

3. SEP Evaluate Claims A friend is observing sparrows in his neighborhood. Each day, he records the number of sparrows he sees. He says that a graph of the data will be a continuous line that rises and falls. Is he correct? Explain.

   Sample: My friend is not correct. He is recording the number of birds seen each day. These are discrete values and would be plotted as separate points on a graph, as bars on a bar graph, not as a straight line.

65B

SAMPLE PROCEDURE (CONTINUED)

C. A student records the temperature of a glass of hot water for 60 minutes as it cools down in a classroom.

   x = amount of time in minutes
   y = temperature of water

D. A geneticist records the number of people in a classroom that have one of the following genetic traits: brown hair, blue eyes, curly hair, left-handedness.

   x = genetic traits (brown hair, blue eyes, curly hair, left-handedness)
   y = number of students

Focus on Mastery!

CCC Patterns Have students analyze their graphs to determine what makes data continuous or discrete. Ask:

- How do your graphs look different?
- If you were performing the investigation described, how would you collect the data? Would you measure it using a tool or collect data using your senses?
- Think about the actual numbers represented in each graph. Can the values be divided? Are the numbers specific to the scenario?

Students should observe that continuous data is measured and can take on any value within a range (i.e., the height of a tree could be any number within a reasonable range). Students should begin to observe that discrete data is counted, the values are distinct, and cannot be divided (i.e., you cannot have half of a student who has brown hair).

HANDS-ON LAB

📄 **GO ONLINE to download...**

this lab and additional teacher support.
Editable

Procedure Tips

- Have students complete the lab in pairs so they can discuss their answers and working definitions of *discrete* and *continuous*. Student graphs should indicate that Scenario A involves continuous data, Scenario B involves discrete data, Scenario C involves continuous data, and Scenario D involves discrete data.
- **Step 2** Students should use graphs to help them determine the differences between continuous and discrete data. For struggling students, consider providing x- and y-axis labels and data sets. Students should find that Scenarios A and C can be graphed using a line graph, but that Scenarios B and D are best represented using bar graphs.

Expected Outcomes

- Upon successfully completing this activity, students will have an understanding of the difference between continuous and discrete data. They will be able to evaluate a data set with the claim that the data contains discrete values.

OBJECTIVES

Students will use text evidence to identify
• the components of a circuit.

Students will apply Ohm's law to describe and calculate how
• changes in resistance change current in a circuit.
• changes in voltage change current in a circuit.

Students will develop models to compare and contrast
• series and parallel circuits.

CONNECT
0.5 class period

📱 **APP** .... (15)
Vocabulary App

🧪 **HANDS-ON LAB** .... (15)
Do the Lights Keep Shining?

LESSON 1 .... (20)
Student Edition

📖 **ETEXT** .... (20)

NEXT GENERATION SCIENCE STANDARDS

MS-PS4-3 Integrate qualitative scientific and technical information to support the claim that digitized signals are a more reliable way to encode and transmit information than analog signals.

DCI PS4.C Information Technologies and Instrumentation Digitized signals (sent as wave pulses) are a more reliable way to encode and transmit information.

CCC.6 Structure and Function Structures can be designed to serve particular functions by taking into account properties of different materials, and how materials can be shaped and used.

SEP.8 Obtaining, Evaluating, and Communicating Information Integrate qualitative scientific and technical information in written text with that contained in media and visual displays to clarify claims and findings.

Connection to Nature of Science Advances in technology influence the progress of science and science has influenced advances in technology.

INVESTIGATE
1–2 class periods

- ▶ **VIDEO** .... ⑤
  Teaching Video

- 🧪 **uInvestigate Lab** .... ⑮
  Electric Current and Voltage

- 👆 **INTERACTIVITY** .... ⑤
  Electric Circuits

SYNTHESIZE
1–2 class periods

- 👆 **INTERACTIVITY** .... ⑩
  Light the Lights

- 🧪 **Quest** CHECK-IN .... ㊵
  Constructing a Microphone

- 📄 **DOCUMENT** .... ⑮
  L3 Enrichment

DEMONSTRATE
0.5 class period

- **LESSON 1** Check .... ⑮
  Student Edition

- ☑ **ASSESSMENT** .... ㉚
  Lesson Quiz

- 📄 **DOCUMENT** .... ⑮
  L1 Remediation

LESSON FEATURES

uEngineer It! STEM

PROTOTYPE TO PRODUCT ⑩
A Life-Saving Mistake

ENGINEERING DESIGN NOTEBOOK .... ⑦⓪
Build a Soccer Practice Partner

👆 **INTERACTIVITY** .... ⑮
Electricity Drives
Your Heartbeat

ELA/LITERACY STANDARDS

RST.6-8.2 Determine the central ideas or conclusions of a text; provide and accurate summary of the text distinct from prior knowledge or opinions.

WHST.6-8.1.B Support claim(s) with logical reasoning and relevant, accurate data and evidence that demonstrate an understanding of the topic or text, using credible sources.

MATHEMATICS STANDARDS

7.RP.A.2 Recognize and represent proportional relationships between quantities.

LESSON
1 Electric Circuits

CONNECT

Objectives

Students will use text evidence to identify
• the components of a circuit.

Students will apply Ohm's law to describe and calculate how
• changes in resistance change current in a circuit.
• changes in voltage change current in a circuit.

Students will develop models to compare and contrast
• series and parallel circuits.

Focus on Mastery!

Connect It! Analyze Systems Make sure that students have identified an item or multiple objects that have circuits. Then have students meet in small groups and answer the following questions.

• What are the components of the circuit? *(Answer depends on the object chosen.)*
• What is the role of each circuit component? *(Answer depends on the object chosen.)*
• The circuit components in the object form a system. What happens if one part of the system is removed? *(The object will not work as intended.)*

Guiding Questions

• What are the components of a circuit?
• How does Ohm's law apply to circuits?
• What is the difference between a series circuit and a parallel circuit?

Connections

Literacy Determine Central Ideas
Math Use Proportional Relationships

MS-PS4-3

HANDS-ON LAB

Investigate Explore Ohm's law in action with your own circuit.

Vocabulary
electrical circuit
voltage
resistance
Ohm's law
series circuit
parallel circuit

Academic Vocabulary
diameter

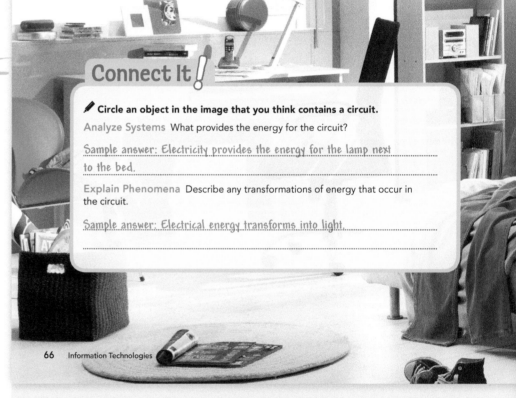

Connect It!

✏ **Circle an object in the image that you think contains a circuit.**

Analyze Systems What provides the energy for the circuit?

Sample answer: Electricity provides the energy for the lamp next to the bed.

Explain Phenomena Describe any transformations of energy that occur in the circuit.

Sample answer: Electrical energy transforms into light.

PROFESSIONAL DEVELOPMENT

Content Refresher

Lesson 1 describes electrical circuits. An electrical circuit has three basic components: a source of electric potential energy such as a battery, a wire that is a conducting path for the electric charges, and one or more devices that transform electric potential energy into other forms of energy. A circuit with only one complete path is a series circuit. A circuit with more than one complete path is a parallel circuit. Lesson 1 reviews three electrical quantities. Voltage of the energy source is the difference in potential electric energy per charge and is measured in volts (V). Current is the rate of movement of charge through the conducting path and is measured in amps (A). Resistance is a measure of how difficult it is for current to move and is measured in ohms (Ω).

NEXT GENERATION SCIENCE STANDARDS

MS-PS4-3 Integrate qualitative scientific and technical information to support the claim that digitized signals are a more reliable way to encode and transmit information than analog signals.

Parts of a Circuit

The wall clock in **Figure 1** is part of an electrical circuit. An **electrical circuit** is a complete, unbroken path that electric charges can flow through.

A circuit consists of a few basic parts: a source of electrical energy, conducting wires, and a device that runs on the electrical energy. In a wall clock batteries are the source of electrical energy. Conducting wires connect the batteries to a motor attached to the clock's arms. The motor runs on electrical energy—converting the batteries' energy to the clock's motions. Circuits sometimes also contain switches. When a switch is closed, charges can flow through the circuit. When a switch is open, the circuit is broken and charges cannot flow. A light switch in your home is used to open and close the circuit that sends electrical energy from a power plant to your light bulb.

Even though energy in circuits is used to power devices, the energy is always conserved. The electrical energy does not get used up—instead, it is transformed from one form to another. For example, in a table lamp, the electrical energy is transformed into light and heat.

HANDS-ON LAB

Build two circuits and see what happens when some of the lights are unscrewed.

Electric Circuits in a Home
Figure 1 Many devices in a typical home contain circuits and use electricity.

67

VOCABULARY APP

Students can practice lesson vocabulary throughout the lesson and before assessments.

HANDS-ON LAB

📄 **GO ONLINE to download…**

Do the Lights Keep Shining? Students build a series circuit with two bulbs and a parallel circuit with two bulbs and investigate what happens in each circuit when one of the lamps is unscrewed. **Editable**

INVESTIGATE

Parts of a Circuit

Connect to the Real World: Inventors Making electricity work requires both scientists and inventors. Thomas Edison and Nikola Tesla are two well-known inventors who worked on electricity generation. Have students pair up and come up with one or two ideas for an invention that is powered by electricity.

Activate Prior Knowledge Have students meet in small groups and answer the following questions.

• What is the source of electrical energy in your home?
• What kinds of devices are used in circuits in your home?
• What is the location of the circuit path when you plug something in?

ELD SUPPORT

ELD.K12.ELL.SC.1

Writing Have students write definitions of vocabulary words using the following leveled strategies throughout the topic.

Entering Have students write the definition of each glossary word in their native language.

Beginning Have students write the definition of each glossary word with a frame that is taken from the text.

Developing Have students locate the definition of each glossary word in the text and copy it.

Expanding Have students write an original definition of each glossary word using the text as a reference.

Bridging Have students write an original definition of each glossary word without using the text as a reference.

LESSON 1

Teach with Movement This activity addresses the Guiding Question: "What are the components of a circuit?" Tell a group of students that they will demonstrate a circuit. Have students stand in a circle, and give each student a square of paper or cardstock that represents electric charge. Designate one student to be a battery. Designate one student to be a switch, and have him or her step outside the circle. Explain that when the switch student steps out of the circuit, that is the same as turning a switch off. Have the switch student turn on the circuit, and have students pass the squares around the circle to show current. Explain that a person can only have one square so everyone has to pass their squares at the same time. Have students move the squares at a rate of about 1 square per 1 second.

Have the switch student turn off the circuit, and designate a student to be a circuit device, a bulb. Explain that a device resists current and the bulb student will hold each square for 2 seconds before handing it on. Explain that this delay affects the whole circuit and everybody has to wait 2 seconds before passing and receiving a square of paper.

Explain that two bulbs would double the resistance and students would hold their squares for 4 seconds. Ask: How does more resistance affect the current? *(Current decreases.)* Make sure the circuit is stopped. Explain that the battery no longer has a difference in electric potential energy between the battery ends. Ask: What is the battery's voltage? *(zero)* Ask: How does zero voltage affect current? *(Current stops.)*

Potential Energy

Figure 2 Objects at higher positions have greater potential energy per unit of mass. Similarly, a battery with a higher voltage has greater electrical potential energy per charge.

SEP Develop Models

✏ Draw an X on the water slide where a person would have the greatest gravitational potential energy per unit of mass. Draw an X on the circuit where it has the greatest electric potential energy per charge.

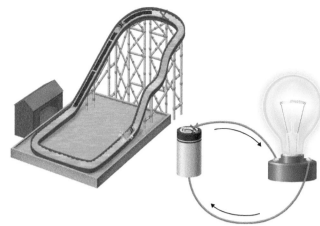

Literacy Connection

Determine Central Ideas What does voltage measure?

It measures the difference in potential energy per charge between two points.

Voltage Electric current flows through a circuit because of differences in electric potential energy in the electric charges. In circuits, it is helpful to think about the electric potential energy per charge, or electric potential, at different points in a circuit. **Voltage** is the difference in electric potential energy per charge between two points in a circuit. So, voltage is the difference in electric potential. Voltage is measured in volts (V).

A typical battery has two ends. One end has a higher electric potential than the other. The end with higher electric potential is called the positive end, and the end with lower electric potential is the negative end. The difference in electric potential is the battery's voltage. For example, the positive end of a 12-volt battery has an electric potential 12 volts higher than the negative end. When the battery is connected within a circuit, this voltage causes current to flow. The current moves from the positive end through the circuit and back to the negative end. The current flows naturally, much like water on a water slide (**Figure 2**).

As the current flows through the circuit, the electric potential energy is converted to other forms of energy. As a result, the electric potential drops as the charges move through the circuit. When the charges reach the battery, they need to regain potential energy if the current is going to continue. The battery supplies the charges with energy by converting chemical energy (from chemicals within the battery) to electrical energy.

The directions of current and voltage were originally defined for positive charges. It was later discovered that negatively-charged electrons flow through a wire circuit. It can be confusing, but remember that what we call electric current goes in the opposite direction of the actual flow of electrons.

PROFESSIONAL DEVELOPMENT

Beyond the Content

Computers use microprocessors to process information. The microprocessor is a complex electrical circuit called an integrated circuit. An integrated circuit has transistors, variable resistors, capacitors, and diodes. These components control the current in an integrated circuit in different ways. A transistor can amplify current and also turn current on or off. A variable resistor can change the amount of current. A capacitor stores charge and releases it all in one quick burst to cause a spike in current that rapidly decreases, and a diode can block or allow current depending on conditions.

Resistance Objects that run on electricity act as resistance to the flow of current. **Resistance** is a measure of how difficult it is for current to flow through an object. It takes more energy for charges to move through objects with higher resistance. Therefore, there is a greater drop in electric potential as the current flows through the circuit. Objects that provide resistance are called resistors. A light bulb, for example, acts as a resistor (**Figure 3**).

The resistance of an object depends on its **diameter**, length, temperature, and material. Objects with a smaller diameter and longer length are more difficult to flow through. In the same way, it is more difficult to sip a drink through a narrow and long straw than a wide and short straw. Current also flows more easily through an object when it is cold than when it is hot. Warmer particles vibrate more and obstruct the flow of current. Current also flows more easily through materials that are good conductors. The conductors have electrons that are more loosely bound, so the charges can move more easily.

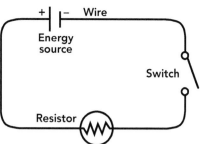

☑ **READING CHECK** **Summarize** What kind of device in a circuit supplies voltage? What kind of device acts as a resistor?

An energy source such as a battery supplies voltage. Objects that use energy or obstruct current flow act as resistors.

Potential Energy

Figure 3 The diagrams show a circuit with a battery, conducting wires, a switch, and a light bulb.

Academic Vocabulary

Student Discourse
Discuss with a classmate how you would describe the diameter of a round wire. Record your response here.

It is the full width of the wire or distance across the face of it.

Model It!

Drawing Circuit Diagrams
As shown in **Figure 3**, symbols are used in a diagram to show the parts of a circuit.

1. SEP Develop Models 🖊 In the space provided, draw what the circuit in **Figure 3** would look like if another battery and another light bulb were added.

2. CCC Cause and Effect Will the total resistance in the circuit increase or decrease when more light bulbs are added? Explain.

Resistance will increase. Light bulbs are resistors, so more of them will provide more resistance.

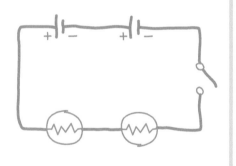

69

Academic Vocabulary

Teach with Visuals Have students draw a wire from two perspectives, looking at it from the side and looking at it straight on. Demonstrate these two perspectives, and have students identify the diameter in both drawings.

Focus on Mastery!

Model It! CCC Cause and Effect Have students draw the circuit with the additional bulbs and label each bulb with an *R* to show the resistance. Verify students' work, and then have students meet in groups and determine what the total resistance of the circuit is in terms of *R*.

SCAFFOLDED QUESTIONS

Use the questions below to assess students' depth of understanding of the content on this page. Have students support their responses with evidence from the text.

Define What does voltage measure? *(difference in electric potential energy per charge between two points in a circuit)* **DOK 1**

Cite Which end of the battery has higher electric potential energy? *(the positive end)* **DOK 1**

Cite As a wire's length increases, how does its resistance change? *(It increases.)* **DOK 1**

Cite As a wire's diameter increases, how does its resistance change? *(It decreases.)* **DOK 1**

Argue How does the electric potential energy per charge change when current flows through a bulb? Include evidence for your argument. *(The energy must decrease since some electric potential energy is converted to light.)* **DOK 3**

DIFFERENTIATED INSTRUCTION

L1 Support Struggling Students
Have students create a chart of the symbols used in circuit drawings. Include a battery symbol, a line for the wire, a resistor symbol, and a switch symbol.

L3 Support Advanced Students
Have students research how a transistor, a capacitor, and a diode affect current. Challenge students to create a chart of the symbols used in circuit drawings that includes symbols for the components in the lesson and for the components they researched.

LESSON 1

INVESTIGATE

Ohm's Law

VIDEO

GO ONLINE to access...
Teaching Video Students delve deeper into a lesson concept.

HANDS-ON LAB

 GO ONLINE to download...

иInvestigate

Electric Current and Voltage Students build a circuit and observe the relationships among voltage, current, and resistance by using different lengths of a graphite pencil. **Editable**

Class Time 15

Group Size groups

Materials (per group) no. 2 pencil with graphite exposed along its length, 25-cm wires with alligator clips on both ends (3), D-cells in a battery holder (2), 3-V light bulb in a socket

Procedure Tips
• In advance, cut the pencils lengthwise with a utility knife, trimming away enough wood to expose the graphite.

Math Toolbox 7.RP.A.2

Use Proportional Relationships Using Ohm's law, demonstrate simple calculations that show patterns between changes in resistance and current and between changes in voltage and current. Guide students to recognize the proportional relationships in Ohm's law using these patterns.

VIDEO

Observe what happens to charges as current flows through a resistor.

HANDS-ON LAB

иInvestigate Explore Ohm's law in action with your own circuit.

Ohm's Law

About 200 years ago, scientist Georg Ohm experimented with electric circuits. He measured the resistance of a conductor and varied the voltage to find the relationship between resistance and voltage. He found that changing the voltage in the circuit changes the current but does not change the resistance of the conductor. When voltage increases, current increases but resistance does not change. Ohm came up with a law for this relationship. **Ohm's law** states that resistance in a circuit is equal to voltage divided by current.

$$\text{Resistance} = \frac{\text{Voltage}}{\text{Current}}$$

Resistance is measured in ohms (Ω). This means that one ohm of resistance is equal to one volt (V) divided by one amp (A). If you increase voltage without changing resistance, then current must increase as well.

Solving this equation for voltage, you obtain:

$$\text{Voltage} = \text{Current} \times \text{Resistance}$$

If you increase the resistance of a circuit without changing the voltage, then the current must decrease.

Math Toolbox
Applying Ohm's Law

A stereo converts electrical energy into sound energy. The stereo is plugged into a wall outlet. The voltage is supplied by a power plant, and the current is carried through electrical wires to the stereo.

1. **Use Proportional Relationships** When you turn up the volume on a stereo, the voltage increases. Assuming the resistance of the stereo remains the same, what happens to the current?
   The current increases.

2. **SEP Use Mathematics** Suppose you turn up the volume on a stereo so that the voltage increases to 110 V while the resistance remains at 55 Ω. Calculate the current after this voltage increase.
   Voltage = Current × Resistance; Current = Voltage / Resistance
   Current = 110 V / 55 Ω = 2 A

PROFESSIONAL DEVELOPMENT

Collaborate with the Community
Have a power company representative or a professional electrician visit the classroom to talk about electrical safety. Have students create posters or pamphlets using the information in the presentation. Display the posters or pamphlets.

Series and Parallel Circuits

Different situations may call for different types of circuits. Suppose a factory uses multiple machines in an assembly line to recycle glass bottles. If the glass-melting machine breaks down but the bottles keep moving, there could be a major safety hazard as the bottles pile up! To prevent this problem, the machines can be wired so that if one machine breaks, then the circuit is broken and all other machines stop working as well. This is called a series circuit.

Series Circuits In a **series circuit**, all parts of the circuit are connected one after another along one path (**Figure 4**). There are advantages to setting up a circuit this way, as in the example of the recycling factory. However, it can sometimes be a disadvantage. The more devices you add to the circuit, the more resistance there is. As you learned with Ohm's law, if voltage remains the same and resistance increases, then current decreases. Adding more light bulbs to a string of lights causes them to shine less brightly. The circuit would have more resistance and the current would decrease, causing the bulbs to appear dimmer.

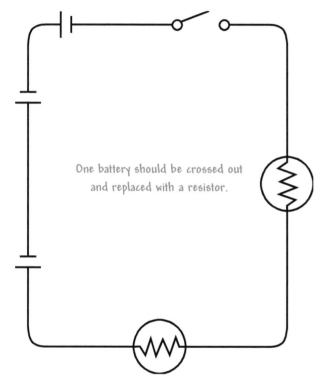

One battery should be crossed out and replaced with a resistor.

 INTERACTIVITY

Explore the similarities and differences between series and parallel circuits.

 Write About It Give one example of a situation in your life in which a series circuit is an advantage, and another example in which it could be a disadvantage.

Correcting Circuit Diagrams
Figure 4 ✎ An electrical engineer draws a circuit diagram of a series circuit that includes three resistors, two batteries, and a switch. SEP Develop Models Find the engineer's mistake, and mark the drawing with your correction.

71

DIFFERENTIATED INSTRUCTION

L1 Support Struggling Students
Scaffold students' use of Ohm's law in problems by providing the equation in three forms along with practice problems. Help students identify which form to use based on the text in each problem.

L3 Support Advanced Students
Have students answer the following question: A parallel circuit has three paths, and the bulbs on each path are the same brightness. Is the voltage across each bulb in the parallel circuit the same or different? Explain your answer. *(The voltage is the same because each bulb has the same amount of energy and voltage measures energy.)*

Series and Parallel Circuits

SCAFFOLDED QUESTIONS

Use the questions below to assess students' depth of understanding of the content on this page. Have students support their responses with evidence from the text.

Calculate What is the current when an 11-ohm hair dryer is connected to a 110-volt source? *(10 amps)* **DOK 1**

Conclude What happens to the brightness of a bulb when there is an increase in voltage? *(The bulb gets brighter.)* **DOK 2**

Explain A person adds a resistor to a bulb and battery circuit in order to decrease the brightness of a bulb. Explain if this solution would work. *(Yes, it would work because the resistance in the circuit would increase and the current would decrease. Less current means a dimmer bulb.)* **DOK 2**

Address Misconceptions Students may think that batteries or generators are the source of electrons in a circuit. Tell students that electrons are within the conducting path and the battery only provides the energy to move the electrons.

🖐 **INTERACTIVITY**

GO ONLINE to access...
Electric Circuits Students compare circuit paths and bulbs' brightness in a series and a parallel circuit and observe what happens when a bulb is removed from each kind of circuit.

📓 **Write About It** WHST.6-8.1.B

This activity addresses the Guiding Question: "What is the difference between a series circuit and a parallel circuit?" Before students write in their notebooks, have students pair up to...

• review the assembly line example in the text and identify a similar situation.

• identify a situation in which a series circuit would not work because each additional device added to the circuit would have less energy.

LESSON 1

SCAFFOLDED QUESTIONS

Use the questions below to assess students' depth of understanding of the content on this page. Have students support their responses with evidence from the text.

Cite If more bulbs are added in series to a circuit, how does the resistance of the circuit change? *(It increases.)* **DOK 1**

Cite If more bulbs are added in parallel to a circuit, how does the resistance of the circuit change? *(It decreases.)* **DOK 1**

True or False A parallel circuit always has more devices than a series circuit. Explain if this statement is true or false. *(It is false. A series circuit can have only one device, but it can also have more devices added in series. A parallel circuit must have at least two devices, but it can also have more devices added in parallel.)* **DOK 2**

Argue Are homes wired in series or parallel? Provide evidence for your argument. *(Homes are wired in parallel because if one device is not working, other devices are not affected.)* **DOK 3**

SYNTHESIZE

 INTERACTIVITY

GO ONLINE to access...

Light the Lights Students examine resistance factors to fix a model by completing a circuit.

What it is A gallery of text and images followed by interactive and short-answer assessments

What it does The interactivity enables the student to evaluate a non-working model and suggest solutions to complete a circuit based on what they know about sources, resistors, closed paths, and switches.

How to use it

Review Ohm's law; discuss what the variables are and how they influence the equation.

INTERACTIVITY

Review the parts of a circuit and fix a set of broken lights.

Parallel Circuits In other situations, you may want each device in a circuit to be wired so that if one device breaks, the others still work. For instance, when one overhead light burns out in the kitchen, you don't expect the other lights to go out, leaving you in the dark. In situations like this, you should use a **parallel circuit**, in which different parts of the circuit are on separate branches. As shown in **Figure 5**, there are several paths for the current to take in a parallel circuit.

Surprisingly, adding resistors in parallel to the circuit actually causes resistance to decrease. How is this possible? Adding a branch opens up another path for current to flow. This is similar to adding another pipe for water to flow through. Therefore, resistance in the circuit decreases and current increases. However, the additional current flows down the new path, so it does not affect the other devices. If a string of lights is set up along a parallel circuit, then each new bulb you add will glow as brightly as those originally on the strand.

☑ **READING CHECK** **Determine Central Ideas** Describe the main difference between a series circuit and a parallel circuit.
A series circuit has all of its devices along one path. A parallel circuit has different branches for different devices.

Light Bulbs in Parallel
Figure 5 The circuit diagram shows three light bulbs in parallel.

1. **CCC Cause and Effect** What happens to the other two light bulbs when one light bulb goes out? Explain.
They keep glowing because they are still connected to the battery. They do not glow any brighter or dimmer.

2. **SEP Develop Models** Draw the circuit again, adding one switch to each branch so that the bulbs can be controlled separately.

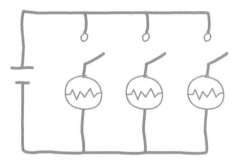

DIFFERENTIATED INSTRUCTION

L1 Support Struggling Students
Have students study the figure **Light Bulbs in Parallel**. Have students identify each kind of component in the circuit.

L3 Support Advanced Students
Have students study the figure **Light Bulbs in Parallel**. Explain that all bulbs in the parallel circuit have the same brightness. Explain that if the circuit were reconfigured to be a series circuit with one bulb, that bulb would also have the same brightness. Ask students to construct an argument using evidence about the relative values of the voltage across each bulb in the parallel and series circuits.

At the Boardwalk

Figure 6 ✏ Many activities at the boardwalk involve circuits. Circle the places where circuits would be.

SEP Construct Explanations Why do you think five of the last lights on the Ferris wheel have gone out?

The Ferris wheel is probably lit using parallel circuits, with each section of lights on a separate circuit. One section is not working, but it does not affect the other sections.

73

SEP Construct Explanations Explain that each path of a parallel circuit can be thought of as series circuits connected to the same energy source. Have students identify which lights are on a single path by noting which lights have gone out.

☑ **READING CHECK** **RST.6-8.2**

Determine Central Ideas Have students create an organizer that describes for each type of circuit...

- the circuit path(s).
- what happens to the other bulbs when one or more bulbs are removed.
- how total resistance changes when one or more bulbs are added.

Assess on the Spot Have students pair up and assess the organizers they created to help them complete the Reading Check. Provide a sample organizer with correct information for the assessment.

📄 **DOCUMENT**

GO ONLINE to download...
L3 Enrichment Extend student understanding of the lesson. **Editable**

PROFESSIONAL DEVELOPMENT

Reflect

Which activity helped students connect bulb brightness and current?

....

....

Which activity helped students understand the difference between series and parallel circuits?

....

....

☑ LESSON 1 Check

 CHECK-IN

 HANDS-ON LAB

📄 **GO ONLINE to download...**

Constructing a Microphone Students identify the different types of analog and digital sound recordings. Students build a model of a microphone and use it to show how sound waves can be converted into electrical signals. Students construct an argument about the changes in energy that occur in a microphone. **Editable**

DEMONSTRATE

Assessment and Remediation

☑ ASSESSMENT

GO ONLINE to access...
Lesson Quiz Formally assess students' learning from the lesson using this auto-graded online assessment. **Editable**

🗎 DOCUMENT

GO ONLINE to download...
L1 Remediation This auto-assigned remediation document provides targeted support for students who struggle on the assessment. **Editable**

Depth of Knowledge

DOK Level	Questions
1	1, 2
2	3
3	4, 5

NEXT GENERATION SCIENCE STANDARDS

MS-PS4-3 Integrate qualitative scientific and technical information to support the claim that digitized signals are a more reliable way to encode and transmit information than analog signals.

☑ LESSON 1 Check

MS-PS4-3

1. Identify What are the three main parts that must be present to make up a circuit?
a source of electrical energy, connecting wires, and a device that runs on the energy

2. Define How is voltage related to electric potential energy?
Voltage is the difference in electric potential energy per charge between two points in a circuit.

3. SEP Develop Models ✏ Draw a series circuit diagram that contains a battery, a switch, and three resistors. Label the parts of the circuit.
Students' drawings should show a battery symbol, switch symbol, and three resistor symbols all connected along the same path.

4. CCC Structure and Function A long, narrow resistor is placed in a series circuit along with a short, wide resistor made of the same material. Which will have a greater electric potential drop across it? Explain your reasoning.
The long, narrow resistor will have the greater voltage drop. It is long and narrow, so it has a higher resistance because resistance increases as diameter decreases and length increases. Higher resistance means greater voltage drop in a series circuit.

5. CCC Cause and Effect Suppose you construct a parallel circuit consisting of a battery, a switch, and four light bulbs. One of the light bulbs goes out. What happens to the brightness of the remaining bulbs? Explain.
The other light bulbs will continue burning as bright as they were before. The branch of the circuit with the burnt-out light bulb no longer provides a path for the current. Current can still flow along the other branches, so the other branches are unaffected.

 CHECK-IN

You have discovered the meaning of voltage and resistance and how they relate to current as described by Ohm's law. You've also read about the different parts of a circuit and how to connect them in series or in parallel.

SEP Communicate Information How might your understanding of circuits help you decide what type of recording device to use?

Sample: I can think about how circuits are used in different types of recording devices. I can decide which device uses circuits efficiently.

 HANDS-ON LAB

Constructing a Microphone

Go online to download the lab worksheet. Develop and use a model that shows how a simple microphone converts sound waves into electrical signals.

Lesson Check Scoring Notes
Assess students' responses to short-answer questions using the rubrics below:

4. CCC Structure and Function DOK 3, 6 points

2pt	Student explains that resistance increases as length increases and as diameter decreases.
2pt	Student explains that higher resistance means a greater drop in electric potential energy (voltage).
2pt	Student concludes that the long narrow resistor has a greater voltage drop.

5. CCC Cause and Effect DOK 3, 4 points

2pt	Student explains that each bulb in a parallel circuit will have its own path to the battery.
2pt	Student concludes that the other bulbs will stay on.

 littleBits CHALLENGE

A LIFE-SAVING
Mistake

 **INTERACTIVITY**

Explore what makes up a pacemaker and how it works.

How do you create a tiny device that saves hundreds of thousands of lives? You engineer it! The story of Wilson Greatbatch shows us how.

The Challenge: To develop the first successful cardiac pacemaker.

Phenomenon In 1956, Greatbatch was working at the University of Buffalo, in New York, as an assistant professor in electrical engineering. He was building an electronic device to record the heart rhythms of cardiac patients. While tinkering with the circuitry, he made a mistake and put a resistor into the circuit that was the wrong size.

When Greatbatch added the resistor, he did not get the outcome he expected. The circuit periodically buzzed with electrical pulses that reminded the engineer of a human heartbeat.

Greatbatch's error turned out to be a happy accident. He realized that the device could help cardiac patients whose hearts beat irregularly. He used the idea to develop the first successful pacemaker, a device that delivers small electrical shocks to the heart muscle to keep it beating regularly and pumping blood normally.

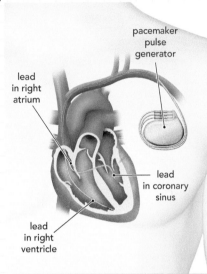

pacemaker pulse generator

lead in right atrium

lead in coronary sinus

lead in right ventricle

A pacemaker uses a pulse generator implanted below a patient's skin to send electric pulses to the heart. The pulses travel through wires called leads.

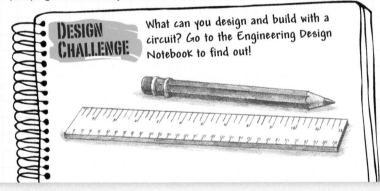

DESIGN CHALLENGE What can you design and build with a circuit? Go to the Engineering Design Notebook to find out!

75

littleBits
CHALLENGE

Go online to access your digital course for student activities and teacher support.

If your students enjoyed this activity, then encourage them to explore and investigate the littleBits challenges in their digital course. These unique opportunities allow students to continue their study of the engineering design process using littleBits electronic building blocks.

 INTERACTIVITY

GO ONLINE to access . . .

Electricity Drives Your Heartbeat Students will discover how pacemakers use electric signals to mimic the heart's natural signal to keep a heart beating, Students will learn the role of electric circuits in pacemakers as part of their interaction.

DESIGN CHALLENGE **Go to the Engineering Design Notebook**

Using Phenomena Students work in groups to design, build, and test a model of a device that automatically hits soccer balls to a goalie. The model will be tested with a table tennis ball. Student groups present their model to the class and consider what needs to be done to scale up the model for a soccer ball.

Class Time (70)

Group Size groups

Materials (per group) 3-volt motor, AA battery and holder, duct tape, ¾-inch rubber faucet washer, paper clips, scissors, wire strippers, aluminum foil, craft sticks or paint stirrers (2), stranded hook-up wire, table tennis ball

Safety
• Tell students to disconnect the circuit if it gets hot and then let you know immediately.
• Tell students to take care working with the wire.
• Tell students to make sure that table tennis balls are not hit toward other students during the testing phase.

Advanced Prep (10)
Gather materials ahead of time for each group.

Classroom Strategies
• After students list the criteria and constraints in their groups, have groups share their ideas in a whole-class discussion.
• Have students help you draw a model of the conversion of energy that takes place in the device.
• If time is short, establish a procedure for students to review their classmates' designs instead of presentations. For example, you could place each model on a desk and have student groups visit each model for one minute.

OBJECTIVES

Students will use evidence from informational texts to compare and contrast
- electronic signals and electromagnetic signals

Students will use models to describe
- digital signals and analog signals.
- how analog signals can be converted to digital signals.

Students will develop models to explain
- how information is encoded into signals, transmitted, and decoded.

CONNECT
0.5 class period

📱 **APP** 15
Vocabulary App

📄 **DOCUMENT** 5
Clocks

LESSON 2 20
Student Edition

📖 **ETEXT** 20

NEXT GENERATION SCIENCE STANDARDS

MS-PS4-3 Integrate qualitative scientific and technical information to support the claim that digitized signals are a more reliable way to encode and transmit information than analog signals.

DCI PS4.C Information Technologies and Instrumentation Digitized signals (sent as wave pulses) are a more reliable way to encode and transmit information.

CCC.6 Structure and Function Structures can be designed to serve particular functions by taking into account properties of different materials, and how materials can be shaped and used.

SEP.8 Obtaining, Evaluating, and Communicating Information Integrate qualitative scientific and technical information in written text with that contained in media and visual displays to clarify claims and findings.

Connection to Nature of Science Advances in technology influence the progress of science and science has influenced advances in technology.

Connection to Engineering, Technology, and Applications of Science Technologies extend the measurement, exploration, modeling, and computational capacity of scientific investigations.

INVESTIGATE
1–3 class periods

👆 **INTERACTIVITY** .... (10)
Analog and Digital Signals

▶ **VIDEO** .... (5)
Teaching Video

🧪 **uInvestigate Lab** .... (20)

Constructing a Simple
Computer Circuit

SYNTHESIZE
1–2 class periods

👆 **INTERACTIVITY** .... (15)
I've Got to Take This Call

👆 **INTERACTIVITY** .... (10)
Digitized Images

👆 **Quest** CHECK-IN .... (10)
Analog and Digital Recordings

📄 **DOCUMENT** .... (15)
L3 Enrichment

DEMONSTRATE
0.5 class period

LESSON 2 Check .... (15)
Student Edition

✅ **ASSESSMENT** .... (30)
Lesson Quiz

📄 **DOCUMENT** .... (15)
L1 Remediation

LESSON FEATURE

Case Study .... (30)

Super Ultra High Definition!

ELA/LITERACY STANDARDS

RST.6-8.2 Determine the central ideas or conclusions of a text; provide and accurate summary of the text distinct from prior knowledge or opinions.

MATHEMATICS STANDARDS

MP.7 Look for and make use of structure.

CONNECT

Objectives

Students will use evidence from informational texts to compare and contrast
• electronic signals and electromagnetic signals.

Students will use models to describe
• digital signals and analog signals.
• how analog signals can be converted to digital signals.

Students will develop models to explain
• how information is encoded into signals, transmitted, and decoded.

Focus on Mastery!

Connect It! SEP Construct Explanations
Implement a Think-Write-Pair-Share strategy using the following questions.

• Identify the signal in the picture. *(the hand gesture)*
• How is the signal transmitted? *(by line of sight)*
• What might be the advantage of this kind of signal? *(It is easy for the dog to see and understand, even from far away.)*

NEXT GENERATION SCIENCE STANDARDS

MS-PS4-3 Integrate qualitative scientific and technical information to support the claim that digitized signals are a more reliable way to encode and transmit information than analog signals.

Guiding Questions

• How is information sent as signals?
• What are digital and analog signals?
• How are signals transmitted?

Connections

Literacy Summarize Text
Math Draw Comparative Inferences

MS-PS4-3

HANDS-ON LAB

иInvestigate Explore how analog signals can be converted to digital information.

Vocabulary	Academic Vocabulary
wave pulse	transmission
electronic signal	
electromagnetic signal	
digital signal	
analog signal	
pixel	

Connect It!

🖊 **Circle the visual signal that is being used to communicate information.**

SEP Construct Explanations Why do you think hand signals are useful for communicating with a dog?

A dog will be able to see and respond to a hand signal from a distance, and without needing any sound. A dog's ability to understand spoken commands may be more limited than its ability to understand hand signals.

PROFESSIONAL DEVELOPMENT

Content Refresher

Lesson 2 describes how information sent as electric current travels as electronic signals and information sent as electromagnetic waves travels as electromagnetic signals. The information in both forms can be analog signals or digital signals. Signals with a continuous set of values are analog. Signals that have a discrete set of values are digital. Analog signals provide a more accurate representation of phenomena such as sound. However, digital signals can be stored on any digital device such as a computer. Digital signals of sound can be created by measuring amplitude and frequency at regular time intervals to produce a discrete set of values, a process called sampling.

Signals and Information

An electric circuit can be used to power a device like a light bulb. However, circuits can also be used to send information. Think about a doorbell, which is usually a circuit. When someone presses a button outside a door, the circuit is complete and the electricity powers a bell that chimes. If you understand the meaning of the chime (a signal that someone is at the door), then you can respond by going to the door. For any signal to be understood, there needs to be agreement between the sender and the receiver about what the signal means. In some cases, the signal can be simple, such as a doorbell or basic hand signals, like the one the pet owner is using in **Figure 1**. Others are more complex. For example, you are reading a specific sequence of letters and spaces on this page to learn about signals.

For much of the 1800s, people communicated with each other over great distances using electrical signals. Samuel Morse patented a version of the electrical telegraph in 1837, and by the Civil War in 1861, there were telegraph lines that carried Morse code from one side of the United States to the other.

HANDS-ON LAB

Compare and contrast analog and digital clocks.

Signaling
Figure 1 A human can teach a dog to respond to visual signals.

VOCABULARY APP

Students can practice lesson vocabulary throughout the lesson and before assessments.

DOCUMENT

GO ONLINE to download...
Clocks Students compare and contrast an analog clock and a digital clock in terms of ease of use, accuracy, and durability. **Editable**

INVESTIGATE

Signals and Information

Connect to the Real World: GPS People use the global positioning system, or GPS, to determine their location. GPS has 24 satellites orbiting Earth. Each satellite constantly sends out radio signals with information about current time and the satellite's position. Radio signals are electromagnetic signals. A GPS receiver receives these signals from the satellites that are closest to it. The receiver can determine its distance from those satellites by using the time of travel of the signal. By processing data from at least four satellites, the receiver can determine its location. Ask: Have you used GPS? What other information besides distance from the satellites does a GPS receiver need in order to show the location? *(a map of the area)*

ELD SUPPORT

ELD.K12.ELL.SI.1, ELD.K12.ELL.SC.1

Listening Read the text on this page, and have students follow along on the page. Then ask the following questions to students at different proficiency levels.

Entering What words stood out?

Beginning Which key words helped you understand what you heard?

Developing To show that you understood what you heard, explain what each paragraph was about.

Expanding How did the words *circuits, information, signal, sender,* and *receiver* help you understand the text?

Bridging Restate what the two paragraphs tell you in your own words.

Focus on Mastery!

Model It! SEP Use Models This activity address the Guiding Question: "How is information sent as signals?" Have students answer the following questions to help them understand Morse code and telegraph signals.

- Study the figure Morse Code. How are letters encoded in Morse code? *(by combinations of dots and dashes)*
- Which letter takes the shortest time to transmit in Morse code? *(E)*
- Which letters take the longest time to transmit in Morse code? *(J, Q, and Y)*
- Why do you think the inventor of Morse code picked E to take the shortest time? *(The inventor thought about how often different letters appear in words. Since E is found in many words, transmission will be faster if its signal is short.)*

Spark a Discussion Explain that the dots and dashes of Morse code transmit information contained in written text. However, Morse code doesn't capture the nuances of speech such as the way a person emphasizes words or changes pitch. The invention of the telephone fixed that problem. Ask students: How has the ability to transmit voices over long distances changed the way people interact?

Morse Code

Figure 2 In Morse code, combinations of short (dot) and long (dash) wave pulses are sent and each combination is translated into a letter.

Electronic Signals

Electronic Signals An electrical telegraph is used to send Morse code as an **electronic signal**, information that is sent as a pattern in a controlled flow of current through a circuit. The telegraph turns the current on and off as the operator taps a device to close and open the circuit, as shown in **Figure 2**. In Morse code, combinations of short (dot) and long (dash) wave pulses stand for the letters of the alphabet and punctuation marks. A **wave pulse** is a pulse of energy that travels through the circuit when it is closed. In Morse code, the letter A is sent and received as "•—", B is "—•••", and so on. This code can be used to send messages, but it is very slow.

Electronic signaling became more useful and widespread when inventors developed ways to transmit information without translating them into code. In 1876, Alexander Graham Bell patented the first telephone. In Bell's telephone, two people spoke into devices that were part of the same circuit. A microphone converted soundwaves in the air—a caller's voice—into electronic signals that would be carried to the receiver somewhere else. At the time, switchboard operators manually connected two telephones into the same circuit. Eventually, switchboards became fully automated.

Model It!

Be a Telegraph Operator

1. CCC Patterns Use the Morse code chart in **Figure 2** to decode the following four lines of code.

   •—— •••• •— —   what
   •• ••• ••••   is
   ••—• ——— •—•   for
   •—•• ••— —• —•—• ••••   lunch

2. SEP Use Models ✏️ Use Morse code to provide an answer to the message you decoded.

78 Information Technologies

PROFESSIONAL DEVELOPMENT

Beyond the Content

While an electronic signal travels through a wire, an electromagnetic signal travels wirelessly. An electromagnetic signal consists of an electromagnetic carrier wave whose values have been modulated (changed) by an information signal. The receiver removes the values of the electromagnetic carrier wave from the electromagnetic signal to obtain the information signal. AM and FM refer to amplitude modulation and frequency modulation.

Electronic Signals	Electromagnetic Signals
signals are in form of wave pulses along a wire	signals are in form of electromagnetic waves
depends on wires	doesn't require wires
slower signals than electromagnetic	faster signals than electronic

Electromagnetic Signals Information sent as patterns of electromagnetic waves such as visible light, infrared waves, microwaves, and radio waves are **electromagnetic signals**. Modern information technologies use a combination of electronic and electromagnetic signals. In 1895, the first radio station transmitted radio wave signals between two points without using an electrical circuit. This launched wireless forms of communication that allowed messages to be transmitted across the globe. Wireless technologies, such as the ones shown in **Figure 3**, now dominate the telecommunications industry. Electromagnetic signals travel at the speed of light, which is much faster than the speed at which current flows through a circuit.

Different types of electromagnetic signals are used for different purposes. Modern mobile phones communicate using microwaves, which are in the ultra-high frequency (UHF) band of the electromagnetic spectrum. Submarines communicate underwater with extremely low frequency (ELF) waves. Optical fibers use visible and infrared light to transmit large amounts of information.

☑ **READING CHECK** Determine Central Ideas What is an electronic signal?

An electronic signal is data or information sent as patterns of electric impulses in a circuit.

From Wired to Wireless

Figure 3 The transition from wired to wireless telecommunications has allowed people to communicate and share information with each other with greater convenience, speed, and quality.

Compare and Contrast
✏ Complete the table to compare and contrast electronic and electromagnetic signals.

79

DIFFERENTIATED INSTRUCTION

L1 Support Struggling Students
Have students identify which devices they use that send electronic signals through wires and which devices send electromagnetic signals through the air.

L3 Support Advanced Students
Fiber optics use electromagnetic signals in the form of light. Have students research fiber optics and explain why light travels only through the fibers and doesn't spread out.

SCAFFOLDED QUESTIONS

Use the questions below to assess students' depth of understanding of the content on this page. Have students support their responses with evidence from the text.

Define What are electromagnetic signals? *(information encoded in the patterns of electromagnetic waves such as visible light, infrared waves, microwaves, and radio waves)* **DOK 1**

Identify What measurable quantity is being transmitted when a telegraph operator sends a Morse code message? *(current wave pulses)* **DOK 1**

Argue What kind of signals did Bell's telephone use? What evidence from the text supports your answer? *(Bell's telephone uses electronic signals because its signals travel through a circuit.)* **DOK 3**

Evaluate What advantages did the telephone have compared to the telegraph? *(It was easier to use and faster. People could speak words into the device instead of having to translate the words into code.)* **DOK 3**

Use Models Compare the path of travel of an electronic signal and an electromagnetic signal. Use your prior knowledge of electrical circuits and electromagnetic waves. *(Electronic signals are current and can only travel through a conducting path, such as a wire. Electromagnetic signals are waves and spread out in all directions from the source.)* **DOK 3**

☑ **READING CHECK** RST.6-8.2

Determine Central Ideas Remind students of reading strategies for scanning text to find the main ideas.

- Search for the key words in the reading passage. *(electronic, signal)*
- Underline all sentences on the page that contain the answer to the question you want to answer. *(data or information sent as patterns of electric impulses in a circuit)*

INVESTIGATE

Analog and Digital Signals

Literacy Connection RST.6-8.2

Summarize Text This activity addresses the Guiding Question: "What are digital and analog signals?" After students have completed underlining the sentences, ask students to meet in pairs and...

- compare what they underlined.
- explain what they think each sentence they underlined means.
- explain how the underlined sentences helped them understand a difference between analog signals and digital signals.

SCAFFOLDED QUESTIONS

Use the questions below to assess students' depth of understanding of the content on this page. Have students support their responses with evidence from the text.

Cite What two examples of data stored in analog signals are given in the text? *(a seismogram, music recorded on vinyl records)* **DOK 1**

Cite What is the advantage of digital signals? *(They can be stored on computers or other digital devices; they take up very little space compared to analog signals.)* **DOK 1**

Interpret If you viewed a waveform of a signal, how would you know if the information represents an analog signal or a digital signal? *(An analog signal has a smooth line without any jumps. A digital signal has steps.)* **DOK 2**

Types of Signals
Figure 4 Analog signals are continuous, whereas digital signals are discrete.

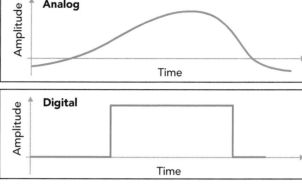

▶ **VIDEO**

Compare analog sound recording devices to newer digital technologies.

Literacy Connection

Summarize Texts
Underline the sentences that summarize the differences between analog and digital signals.

Analog and Digital Signals

Electronic and electromagnetic signals can carry information from one place to another in two different ways: as analog signals or as digital signals. Both analog and digital signals have strengths and weaknesses, but the power and flexibility of digital signals have made them the foundation of modern information technologies.

Analog Signals An **analog signal** allows for a continuous record of some kind of action (**Figure 4**). For example, when seismic waves from an earthquake cause the ground to move, a seismograph records that continuous motion as an analog signal. The advantage of analog signals is that they provide the highest resolution of an action by recording it continuously. But analog signals can be difficult to record. The signals processed by a seismograph must be recorded with ink on paper as a seismogram. Other examples of analog signals are the recordings of music on vinyl records. You can slow down a record and still hear continuous music. However, vinyl records scratch and warp very easily. Analog media also take up a lot of space, compared to digital media.

Digital Signals A **digital signal** allows for a record of numerical values of an action at a set of continuous time intervals (**Figure 4**). This results in a series of numbers. For example, a digital seismometer can record ground motion by recording the numerical value of the ground height at each second. This produces a list of numbers that shows the ground motion, second by second. The disadvantage of digital signals is that you do not have a record of any signals that occurred in between each sampling. One advantage is that once you have recorded the signal as a set of numbers, you can store it on a computer or other digital device. Digital recordings can also be edited easily by just changing the numbers.

PROFESSIONAL DEVELOPMENT

Collaborate with the Community

There is a continuing debate about whether digital recordings of music can ever sound as good as analog recordings. Some people say that improvements in sampling rates mean there is no longer any discernable difference in the two methods of recording sound. Others disagree. Have an expert on sound recording in the community visit the classroom and give a brief overview of sound recording and give his or her opinion on this issue.

Sampling Rate The quality of digital media depends on the length of the recording intervals. The term *sampling rate* refers to how often a signal is recorded or converted to digital code. More data are captured and recorded the more times the event is sampled (**Figure 5**). For example, a digital music file with a high sampling rate may sound richer and more detailed than a file with a lower sampling rate. The downside of a higher sampling rate is that the file size is larger.

Scientists and music producers have conducted tests with people to find a sampling rate that will produce digital music files that sound realistic without having more data than humans can perceive. If the sampling rate is too high and the files are too large, then the files will waste space on music players, mobile phones, computers, or storage services.

 INTERACTIVITY

Compare analog and digital signals, and learn about signal noise.

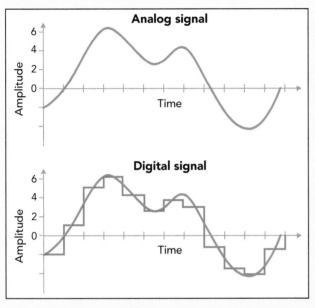

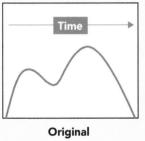 **Original**

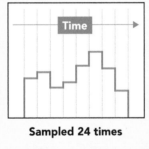 **Sampled 24 times**

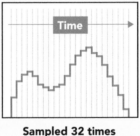 **Sampled 32 times**

Analog-to-Digital Processing

Figure 5 When an analog signal is converted to a digital signal, what was continuous must be broken into discrete pieces. The higher the sampling rate, the closer the digital signal will come to the analog signal.

SEP Develop Models Draw two digital versions of the original analog signal in the blank graphs: one based on sampling the analog signal 24 times, and the other based on sampling 32 times.

81

DIFFERENTIATED INSTRUCTION

L3 Support Advanced Students

Have students pair up and discuss which would have fewer data when encoded in a digital signal, a text message or a voice call using the same number of words. Have students support their argument with evidence.

 **INTERACTIVITY**

GO ONLINE to access...
Analog and Digital Signals Students compare and contrast waveforms of electronic analog signals and electronic digital signals. Students describe the fidelity and efficiency of each kind of signal.

VIDEO

GO ONLINE to access...
Teaching Video Students delve deeper into a lesson concept.

Teach with Visuals Draw a picture of a wave at the front of the classroom. Explain that the sampling is being done on spoken words, which are shown by the wave. Conversion into digital signals will allow the information to be transmitted from one cell phone to another.

Draw points at regular intervals on the wave to show when it will be sampled. At the first sampling point, draw the digital signal in a different color. Show that the digital signal remains at the same value of amplitude by drawing a horizontal line until the next sampling point.

At the next sampling point, draw a vertical line from the horizontal line of the digital signal to the sampling point on the wave. Then again draw a horizontal line for the digital signal with this new value of amplitude. Repeat and continue. The digital signal will have the appearance of steps due to the horizontal and vertical lines. Label each step with its value of amplitude, and tell students that this is what is used to represent the original analog wave. Explain that the analog wave has values of amplitude that correspond to all the points on its line. Ask the following questions:

• Compare the number of values of amplitude in the two kinds of signals. *(The analog signal has more values of amplitude, and the digital signal has fewer values of amplitude.)*
• Which signal uses fewer data points to show the information? *(the digital signal)*
• Which signal shows the information more accurately? *(the analog signal)*

LESSON 2

☑ **READING CHECK** RST.6-8.2

Summarize Text Model a strategy for scanning text for specific information by asking students to...

- underline the key words in the Reading Check task. *(signals, stored, processed, and computers)*
- underline all sentences on the page that contain forms of least two key words. *(the last two sentences of the first paragraph, the first sentence of the third paragraph, and possibly the last sentence of the third paragraph since digital devices includes computers)*

HANDS-ON LAB

📄 **GO ONLINE to download...**

иInvestigate

Constructing a Simple Computer Circuit Students develop a model of a computer using an electric circuit and use the model to encode and transmit analog numbers as digitized signals. **Editable**

Class Time (20)

Group Size groups

Materials (per group) 1.5-V bulbs with sockets (3), 1.5-V dry cell, single pole-single throw knife switches (3), double pole-single throw knife switch, connecting wires, pegboard, machine screws or clips for connecting wires (12)

Procedure Tip At least one bulb should be lit when a switch is closed. If any of the bulbs does not light, then make sure all the connections are making firm contact. Test the bulbs to be certain they are not burned out. Test the battery.

HANDS-ON LAB

иInvestigate Explore how analog signals can be converted to digital information.

Binary Code

Figure 6 The binary codes, or bytes, for the first five letters of the alphabet are shown here. Notice that there are different codes for lowercase and uppercase letters.

a = 01100001 A = 01000001
b = 01100010 B = 01000010
c = 01100011 C = 01000011
d = 01100100 D = 01000100
e = 01100101 E = 01000101

SEP Interpret Data What would the code be for the word *Dad*?

01000100 01100001 01100100

Binary Signals Recall that Morse code has just two signals—dots and dashes—that are used in different combinations to communicate letters. Computers use a similar system called binary, which consists of ones and zeros. The information that we store on computers is encoded with binary, whether it's a song, a text document, or a movie.

Each number in binary code is a bit of information. Bits are arranged into groups of eight, called bytes. The code for each letter of the alphabet has its own unique byte, as shown in **Figure 6**. The code for a word consists of bytes strung together. For example, as the author wrote this page, a computer program translated the keyboard strokes for the letters in the word *"code"* into bytes.

01100011 01101111 01100100 01100101

The basic unit of a computer's storage capacity is the byte. A megabyte is one million bytes. This means one megabyte (MB) can hold a million letters of the alphabet. Digital storage has improved so much in recent years that we now use even larger units such as gigabyte (billion bytes) and terabyte (trillion bytes) to describe the storage capacities of our digital devices.

☑ **READING CHECK** **Summarize Text** How are signals stored and processed on computers?
They are stored in binary code, which consists of 1's and 0's.

Math Toolbox
Cryptography

Cryptography is the study of codes. Use the chart in **Figure 6** to answer the following questions and "break" the codes.

1. **CCC Patterns** What do you think the binary codes for the letters *f* and *F* are?
f = 01100110; F = 01000110

2. **Draw Comparative Inferences** The binary code for the number 6 is 00110110. How does this compare to the code for *f*? What can you infer about the structures of these codes?
The last four digits are the same, because f is the sixth letter of the alphabet. The first four digits are different for letters and numbers. 0110 = lowercase letter; 0011 = number

---

PROFESSIONAL DEVELOPMENT

Beyond the Content

The first computer was invented in the 19th century by English mathematics professor Charles Babbage. He called the machine an Analytical Engine. From 1937 to 1946, improvements were made to the Analytical Engine by adding vacuum tubes to process information. However, these computers had no operating system and could only perform one task. From 1947 to 1962, the computer was again improved by replacing vacuum tubes with transistors and by adding memory, operating systems, and media storage. During this period, the first computer for commercial use was introduced to the public, and more than 100 computer programming languages were developed. In 1963, integrated circuits were added to computers, and the modern computer was born. Continual improvements since that time have made computers easier to use, more powerful, faster, and smaller.

Transmitting Signals

Modern forms of communication involve the **transmission** of electronic or electromagnetic signals. Many transmissions are now in digital formats. In some cases, the transmission consists of an entire file, such as a digital song file saved to your phone. In other cases, the transmission is more like a broadcast, such as a live stream.

Sound Information Analog telephones transmit signals by first converting sound waves to electronic wave pulses. Those travel along wires to another phone, which converts the wave pulses back to sound waves. Modern mobile phones convert sound waves to digital data in the form of binary code. The data are transmitted as microwaves, which are converted back to sound waves by another mobile phone. If someone records and sends a voice message from one mobile phone to another, or to a computer, the process is basically the same. Sound waves are the initial signal and the ultimate product.

INTERACTIVITY

Analyze a model of how phone calls are made with mobile devices.

Academic Vocabulary

In your science notebook, record other uses of the term *transmission* in science. In those other contexts, what's being transmitted?

Digital Audio

Figure 7 To transmit a sound signal from one place to another, the signal must be processed and converted into different forms.

SEP Develop Models ✏ Complete the diagram by identifying the type of signals that are being transmitted.

sound waves

electronic wave pulses

digital signals

sound waves

electronic wave pulses

83

Math Toolbox  MP.7

Draw Comparative Inferences Remind students that a computer is a machine, and have students answer the following questions.

- What is the length of all the codes for letters and numbers shown on this page? *(one byte, which is eight bits)*
- People usually use the overall shapes of letters and numbers to recognize them. Can a computer do this? Why or why not? *(It cannot. A computer can only process information in terms of individual bits.)*
- Review the codes for all the letters and numbers shown on the page. Which information in the byte do you think tells a computer if it is a lowercase letter, an uppercase letter, or a number? *(the first four bits)*

Transmitting Signals

INTERACTIVITY

GO ONLINE to access...

I've Got to Take This Call Students examine digitized signals as a reliable way to encode and transmit information.

What it is Text followed by an interactive exercise and short-answer assessments

What it does Students compare and contrast telephone technologies by applying knowledge of the transfer and transformation of energy and signal noise in a cell phone call.

How to use it

- Ask students what it means to be *in service* or *out of service*. What do cell phones require access to in order to transmit information?

DIFFERENTIATED INSTRUCTION

L1 Support Struggling Students

Read the third and fourth sentences in the first paragraph under the heading *Sound Information* to students, and have them follow along. Explain that modern mobile phones are the same as cell phones. Explain that microwaves are similar to light and travel in the same way by spreading out. Guide students to work in groups to make a diagram of the cell phone processes of encoding, transmitting, and decoding the sound signal. Have students use a stylized wave to show the sound and a stylized stepped waveform to show the digital signal. Have students copy their diagram onto poster paper. Display the finished posters.

LESSON 2

 INTERACTIVITY

GO ONLINE to access...
Digitized Images Students explore the process of encoding images into pixels and compare it to the process of encoding information into digital signals.

SCAFFOLDED QUESTIONS

Use the questions below to assess students' depth of understanding of the content on this page.

Define What does *transmission* mean as it is used on this page? *(Sending information in the form of a signal from one place to another.)* **DOK 1**

Summarize What is the main difference between an analog telephone and a modern mobile phone (cell phone)? *(The analog phone converts sound to electronic wave pulses, and the cell phone converts sound to digital data in the form of binary code.)* **DOK 2**

Model What is the relationship between picture blurriness and number of pixels? *(The greater the number of pixels in a given area, the less blurry a picture appears.)* **DOK 2**

Evaluate Is the process of digitizing a picture similar to sampling? Why or why not? *(It is similar to sampling because one color is picked for each pixel.)* **DOK 3**

 DOCUMENT

GO ONLINE to download...
L3 Enrichment Extend student understanding of the lesson. **Editable**

NEXT GENERATION SCIENCE STANDARDS

MS-PS4-3 Integrate qualitative scientific and technical information to support the claim that digitized signals are a more reliable way to encode and transmit information than analog signals.

 **INTERACTIVITY**

Model how the number of pixels affects the resolution of digital images.

Pixels and File Size
Figure 8 The three images of the flower are copies of the same file. The leftmost image has a low resolution and small file size. The middle image has higher resolution and a larger file size. The rightmost image has the highest resolution and largest file size.

Visual Information Photographs, printed documents, and other visuals can be digitized and transmitted as well. A digital visual consists of **pixels**, or small uniform shapes that are combined to make a larger image (**Figure 8**). The information that determines a pixel's color and brightness is coded in bytes. The more pixels that are used, the more bytes the digital image file will require. For example, a digital image that is meant to take up a few centimeters on a mobile phone screen may be far less than a megabyte, whereas an image that is meant to be shown on a high-resolution display or printed as a poster can be 50 megabytes and more. Just as audio engineers and music producers try to balance file size with detail that will be audible to human ears, visual artists and engineers must strike a balance too. They don't want their images to appear too "pixilated," but they don't want to waste device storage with too much detail either.

☑ **READING CHECK** **Summarize Text** How are pixels used to capture and convey visual information with digital technology? Pixels are the subunits of digital images. They capture information about color and brightness. This information is encoded as binary for storage and transmission.

PROFESSIONAL DEVELOPMENT

Reflect
Which of the activities in this lesson seemed to best promote students' understanding of the difference between digital signals and analog signals?

What will you do differently the next time you teach about digital signals and analog signals?

☑ LESSON 2 Check

1. **Identify** Sound waves move from a guitar to a microphone. The microphone converts the sound waves to electronic wave pulses that are transmitted through a wire to a computer. The computer converts the wave pulses to a series of 1's and 0's. The 1's and 0's are packaged as a file and posted online for sale to the guitarist's fans. In this process, when were the signals digital?

When the signals were encoded as binary by the computer and packaged as a music file for sale online, they were digital.

2. **SEP Use Mathematics** If one letter of the alphabet is one byte, and the average word consists of five letters, how many words could be encoded in binary and stored on a 1-GB memory card?

1 billion bytes ÷ 5 bytes/word = 200 million words

3. **Make Comparative Inferences** How is the sampling rate used in recording digital music similar to the number of pixels in a digital image?

The number of pixels is basically the same as a sampling rate. The higher the rate or number of pixels, the higher the resolution or fidelity of the recording.

4. **CCC Patterns** Compare and contrast Morse code and binary code.

Sample: They are both digital signal encoding systems. The only major difference is 1 and 0 vs. short and long and the codes used for letters and numbers.

Quest CHECK-IN

In this lesson, you learned about different types of signals and how they are used to record and transmit information.

Evaluate Why is it important to know the different types of signals that can be used to record information?

They have different benefits and drawbacks. Analog signals can be recorded continuously and with higher fidelity, but the recordings can be inaccurate and take up more physical space. Digital signals are easy to record, store, transmit, and even edit, but they are incomplete because they cannot be recorded continuously.

INTERACTIVITY

Analog and Digital Recordings

Go online to investigate and identify advantages and disadvantages of digital music.

85

☑ LESSON 2 Check

Quest CHECK-IN

INTERACTIVITY

GO ONLINE to access...
Analog and Digital Recordings Students describe how a song produced by a singer is made into a digital recording and discuss how the sound of the recording differs from live sound. Students identify the advantages and disadvantages of analog and digital recordings.

DEMONSTRATE

Assessment and Remediation

ASSESSMENT

GO ONLINE to access...
Lesson Quiz Formally assess students' learning from the lesson using this auto-graded online assessment. **Editable**

DOCUMENT

GO ONLINE to download...
L1 Remediation This auto-assigned remediation document provides targeted support for students who struggle on the assessment. **Editable**

Lesson Check Scoring Notes

Assess students' responses to short-answer questions using the rubrics below:

3. Make Comparative Inferences
DOK 3, 4 points

2pt	Student explains that creating pixels with one color each is similar to creating pulses with one value each during sampling.
2pt	Student explains that when more pixels are created or sampling rate is higher, the digitized information has better resolution or fidelity.

4. CCC Patterns DOK 3, 4 points

2pt	Student accurately describes similarities between Morse code and binary code.
2pt	Student accurately describes differences between Morse code and binary code.

Depth of Knowledge

DOK Level	Questions
1	2
2	1
3	3, 4

Purpose

Using Phenomena High-definition televisions are very popular with consumers. These televisions use a greater number of pixels than others, which means that the pictures are sharper and can be viewed at a larger size. In this case study, students learn how increasing the resolution, or definition, of data requires improvements in both hardware and software to represent and transmit the extra amounts of data. Students learn that each pixel takes up 1 byte of data and discover how to complete calculations about data amounts.

Class Time 30

Group Size pairs

Classroom Strategies

- Have students read the text through once with their partner. While reading, have them code the margins with an exclamation point (!) to indicate something interesting they learned, a question mark (?) to ask a question they have about the text, a capital L (L) to indicate something new they learned, and a capital K (K) to indicate something they knew before they read the text.
- Ask students to explain how they think images are converted into digital signals. Students should understand that values of color are measured at regular intervals of space and used to produce a discrete set of values for each pixel.
- Ask students to explain how increasing the number of pixels affects how a picture appears.
- Ask students to explain how increasing the number of pixels affects how large a picture can be displayed.
- Review the meanings and abbreviations of *bits*, *bytes*, *megabits*, *megabytes*, and *gigabytes*.

NEXT GENERATION SCIENCE STANDARDS

MS-PS4-3 Integrate qualitative scientific and technical information to support the claim that digitized signals are a more reliable way to encode and transmit information than analog signals.

MS-PS4-3

Super Ultra High Definition!

If your family has purchased a new television recently, you know there are many digital options. In fact, many consumers and digital media providers have sometimes struggled to keep up with the technological changes.

Video resolution is one of the most important factors in digital TV technology. Resolution refers to the number of pixels on the TV screen. The diagram shows the different resolutions currently in use. The numbers shown for each resolution refer to the dimensions of the screen image in pixels. For example, standard-definition resolution (SD) has a 640 × 480 pixel dimension. The image is made up of 480 horizontal lines. Each line contains 640 pixels, for a total of 307,200 pixels.

As resolution increases, image quality increases because there are more pixels to form the image. However, as resolution and image quality increase, file size increases too. Each pixel in the image takes up 1 byte of storage.

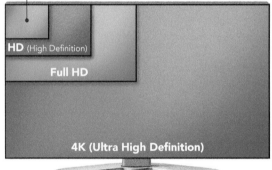

SD (Standard Definition)

HD (High Definition)

Full HD

4K (Ultra High Definition)

This means that one frame of an SD image takes up 307,200 bytes, or about 0.3 megabytes (MB) of storage. A moving TV image runs at 30 frames per second, so a one-hour program would take up about 32,400 MB in storage. This is where video codecs come in. A codec is software that digitally encodes and compresses the video signal to reduce its file size without affecting image quality very much.

PROFESSIONAL DEVELOPMENT

Collaborate with Colleagues

Create a lesson with the art teacher that connects visual art, color, and digital images. The lesson can explain how optical theories developed by visual artists in the 1880s paved the way for digital images. One influential artist was Georges Seurat, who developed a style called *pointillism*. In this style, painters paint tiny dots of pure color side by side to create a complete image when seen from a distance. These tiny dots were the forerunners of pixels.

A Streaming Society

Today, many people download or stream TV shows and movies to their televisions and smart devices. Because the higher-quality signals are larger in file size, fast Internet speeds are required to move all the data. Internet speed is generally measured in megabits per second (Mbps). The amount of data that can be transferred at three different speeds is shown here.

Mbps speed	MB transferred per second
1	0.125
50	6.25
100	12.5

Use the text and data to answer the following questions.

1. **Use Models** A 4K image contains 8,294,400 pixels. What is the corresponding file size?

   It would take up about 8.3 MB of storage.

2. **Calculate** Suppose you're downloading a movie that is 3.2 GB. Your Internet speed is 50 Mbps. About how long will it take to download the file? Show your work.

   It will take about 9 minutes to download the file. 3.2 GB = 3,200 MB.

   A speed of 50 Mbps downloads 6.25 MB per second.

   So, 3,200 ÷ 6.25 = 512 seconds = about 9 minutes.

3. **Patterns** Some video engineers are already touting 8K resolution, the next advance in video technology. The image quality of an 8K signal is equal to taking four 4K TVs and arranging them in a 2 × 2 array. What are the dimensions of an 8K image? Explain.

   An 8K image is twice the height and width of a 4K image. So the resolution of an 8K image is 7,680 × 4,320 pixels.

4. **Analyze Properties** Television programs used to be transmitted using analog signals. As more people began to buy HD televisions and watch HD programming, TV broadcasters and cable providers switched to digital signals. Why do you think this switch occurred? What advantage does a digital signal have over an analog signal when transmitting HD video?

   Sample: An HD program consists of a lot of data. An analog signal would have to carry all the data, but a digital signal can encode and compress the data. This results in less data needing to be transmitted.

5. **Construct Explanations** Most televisions sold now are 4K Ultra HD capable. However, most streaming services and digital TV providers offer little 4K programming. Why do think this is the case?

   Sample: Other technology that is required to stream and watch 4K programs still needs to catch up with the TV technology. Internet service providers and companies that sell digital movies, for example, may need new equipment and new software in order to offer programming at higher resolutions.

87

DIFFERENTIATED INSTRUCTION

L1 Support Struggling Students

Have students create small matrices and use them to show that the multiplication of the number of squares along the top and side equals the total number of squares in the matrix. Connect this exercise to calculating the number of pixels in a specific resolution.

L3 Support Advanced Students

Ask students to explain why specific resolutions are needed for digital video.

 Focus on Mastery!

Calculate Guide students in answering the following questions.

- What does GB stand for? *(gigabyte)*
- What does MB stand for? *(megabyte)*
- How many MB are in 1 GB? *(1,000)*
- How many MB are in the 3.2 GB file? *(3,200)*
- What does Mbps stand for? *(megabits per second)*
- How many bits equal 1 byte? *(8)*
- How many Mb equal 1 MB? *(8)*
- How would you convert 50 Mb to MB? Write down the equation you use. *(50 Mb x MB/8 Mb = 6.25 MB)*
- Write the Internet download speed in MB/s based on the calculation you just did. *(6.25 MB/s)*
- How many seconds will it take to download the 3,200 MB file from the Internet? Write down the equation you use. *(3,200 MB x 1 s/6.25 MB = 512 s)*
- How many minutes will it take to download the 3,200 MB file from the Internet? Write down the equation you use. *(512 s x 1 min/60 s = 8.5 min)*

Scoring Notes

Use the grading rubrics to assess students' responses.

4. **Analyze Properties** DOK 3, 5 points

1pt	Student explains that HD resolution contains more data than SD resolution.
2pt	Student explains that using digital signals rather than analog signals of HD reduces data amount transmitted.
2pt	Student explains that using digital signals reduces data amount transmitted because digital signals can be compressed by codec software.

5. **Construct Explanations** DOK 3, 5 points

1pt	Student explains that digital video with 4K resolution has much more data than digital video with HD resolution.
2pt	Student explains that new equipment is needed to create digital video with 4K resolution.
2pt	Student explains that current download speeds are not fast enough to stream digital video with 4K resolution.

Communication and Technology

OBJECTIVES

Students will use evidence from informational texts on communications technologies to identify
- different kinds of technologies.
- the use of each kind of technology.
- benefits and drawbacks of the use of analog signals and digital signals in each technology.

Students will develop models of the transmission of analog and digital signals in order to support
- the claim that digital signals are more reliable and efficient overall than analog signals.

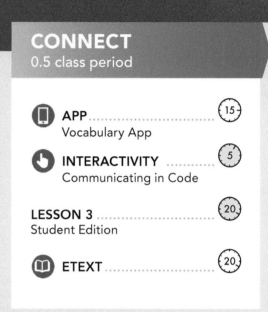

CONNECT
0.5 class period

APP 15
Vocabulary App

INTERACTIVITY 5
Communicating in Code

LESSON 3 20
Student Edition

ETEXT 20

NEXT GENERATION SCIENCE STANDARDS

MS-PS4-3 Integrate qualitative scientific and technical information to support the claim that digitized signals are a more reliable way to encode and transmit information than analog signals.

DCI PS4.C Information Technologies and Instrumentation Digitized signals (sent as wave pulses) are a more reliable way to encode and transmit information.

CCC.6 Structure and Function Structures can be designed to serve particular functions by taking into account properties of different materials, and how materials can be shaped and used.

SEP.8 Obtaining, Evaluating, and Communicating Information Integrate qualitative scientific and technical information in written text with that contained in media and visual displays to clarify claims and findings.

Connection to Nature of Science Advances in technology influence the progress of science and science has influenced advances in technology.

Connection to Engineering, Technology, and Applications of Science Technologies extend the measurement, exploration, modeling, and computational capacity of scientific investigations.

INVESTIGATE
1–3 class periods

👆 **INTERACTIVITY** .... 🕐15
Technology and Communication

▶ **VIDEO** .... 🕐5
Career Video

▶ **VIDEO** .... 🕐5
Teaching Video

👆 **INTERACTIVITY** .... 🕐20
Film Cameras and Digital Cameras

📱 **VIRTUAL LAB** .... 🕐20

🧪 **ᴜInvestigate Lab** .... 🕐30

Let the Music Play

SYNTHESIZE
1–2 class periods

🕐 **INTERACTIVITY** .... 🕐10
Signal Reliability

👆  **CHECK-IN** .... 🕐40
Evaluate Recording
Technologies

📄 **DOCUMENT** .... 🕐15
L3 Enrichment

DEMONSTRATE
0.5 class period

LESSON 3 Check .... 🕐15
Student Edition

☑ **ASSESSMENT** .... 🕐30
Lesson Quiz

📄 **DOCUMENT** .... 🕐10
L1 Remediation

LESSON FEATURE

EXTRAORDINARY SCIENCE ... 🕐15
Beam Me Up!

ELA/LITERACY STANDARDS

RST.6-8.1 Cite specific textual evidence to support analysis of science an technical texts.
RST.6-8.2 Determine the central ideas or conclusions of a text; provide an accurate summary of the text distinct from prior knowledge or opinions.

MATHEMATICS STANDARDS

MP.4 Model with mathematics.
8.F.5 Describe qualitatively the functional relationship between two quantities by analyzing a graph (e.g., where the function is increasing or decreasing, linear or nonlinear). Sketch a graph that exhibits the qualitative features of a function that has been described verbally.

CONNECT

Objectives

Students will use evidence from informational texts on communications technologies to identify
- different kinds of technologies.
- the use of each kind of technology.
- benefits and drawbacks of the use of analog signals and digital signals in each technology.

Students will develop models of the transmission of analog and digital signals in order to support
- the claim that digital signals are more reliable and efficient overall than analog signals.

Focus on Mastery!

Connect It! Compare and Contrast To help students compare and contrast the clay tablet and a personal digital device such as a computer, tablet, or smartphone, have them answer the following questions:

- Compare the shapes of the clay tablet and the digital device.
- What kinds of information are displayed by the clay tablet and the digital device?
- Can more information be added to and displayed on the clay tablet and the digital device?
- Can the clay tablet and the digital device each be used to transmit information to another clay tablet or device?

📱 VOCABULARY APP

Students can practice lesson vocabulary throughout the lesson and before assessments.

NEXT GENERATION SCIENCE STANDARDS

MS-PS4-3 Integrate qualitative scientific and technical information to support the claim that digitized signals are a more reliable way to encode and transmit information than analog signals.

LESSON 3 Communication and Technology

Guiding Questions
- What technologies are used for communication?
- What are the advantages of using digital signals for communications technology?

Connections

Literacy Cite Textual Evidence

Math Analyze Relationships

MS-PS4-3

HANDS-ON LAB

uInvestigate Observe the structure of a vinyl record and predict how it functions.

Vocabulary	Academic Vocabulary
information	hardware
technology	
software	
noise	
bandwidth	

Connect It!

✏️ **Circle a symbol on the clay tablet that appears more than once.**

Compare and Contrast How is the ancient clay tablet similar to a digital tablet of today? How is it different?

Sample answer: Both are relatively flat, with characters used to share or record information. The clay tablet could be used only once and for a limited amount of information. A digital tablet is a computer that can share vast amounts of information.

PROFESSIONAL DEVELOPMENT

Content Refresher

Lesson 3 explains how information technology depends on both hardware and software. Software enables the user to encode, decode, interpret, and manipulate data, while hardware is the physical structure in which data are stored and analyzed. Lesson 3 describes different examples of communication technologies: radio and television, telephones, satellites, fiber optics, and Internet and Wi-Fi. These technologies transmit electronic signals through wires, electromagnetic transmissions through the atmosphere, and electromagnetic transmissions through fiber-optic cables. Digital signals require less bandwidth to carry information than analog signals, can be easily encrypted to ensure security, and are less affected by noise than analog signals.

The Information Age

The invention of writing was one of the first examples of information technology. Using a sharpened stick or a finger and some kind of medium such as clay (**Figure 1**) or a stone wall, people were able to record ideas, observations, and other information.

Fast forward to today. Information technology is everywhere, and there many forms and modes of writing. For example, one person typed the text on this page into a computer. The file was then sent via the internet to reviewers and editors. Edited text was then combined with the photograph in a different computer application. Finally, a file was sent to a printer, and a series of pages were put together as a book. What would have taken hours to inscribe in clay or rock can now be recorded and shared much faster, thanks to information technology. Modern **Information technology** consists of computer and telecommunications **hardware** and software that store, transmit, receive, and manipulate information. **Software** refers to programs that encode, decode, and interpret information, including browsers, apps, games, and operating systems. The invention of electronic computers around 1940 helped usher in the information age.

 INTERACTIVITY

Discuss the encoding and decoding of information with classmates.

Academic Vocabulary

Hardware is an older term. What do you think "hard" refers to in the information technology usage of *hardware*?

It refers to the physical components of the technology.

Sumerian Tablet

Figure 1 This clay tablet was used to record information 6,500 years ago in Sumer, part of Mesopotamia.

89

 **INTERACTIVITY**

GO ONLINE to access...
Communicating in Code Students identify a code they've used and explain how they created and deciphered the coded messages.

INVESTIGATE

The Information Age

Connect to the Real World: Cell Phones The number of cell phones used worldwide is almost five billion. It's the *cell* in cell phones that makes these devices work. Cells are small hexagonal areas of land, each equipped with its own cell tower. Every cell phone caller must use a frequency different from other nearby callers; within each cell, all frequencies can be used. Since cell phones give off weak signals that do not go far, two people in adjacent cells can use the same frequency without mixing up their messages. When you make a call, the cell tower near you receives your signal and relays it to the cell tower that is near the person you are calling. When you talk on your cell phone, you are using two different frequencies of waves: one frequency for the signal that is sent and another frequency for the signal that is received. Ask students: How do you think the sizes of cells compare between a rural area and a city? (*There are more people in a city, so the cells would be smaller in order to ensure that there are enough frequencies for all cell phone users in the area.*)

Academic Vocabulary

Activate Prior Knowledge Ask students the following questions about the word *hardware*.

- Where have you heard or seen the word *hardware* before? What meanings does it have? (*It can mean tools and parts, as in a hardware store. It can mean machinery, as in military hardware.*)
- What do you think *hardware* means when used in information technology? (*the physical parts of a computer or electronic system*)

ELD SUPPORT

ELD.K12.ELL.SI.1, ELD.K12.ELL.SC.1

Reading Use these questions for the two-page spread *Advantages of Digital Signals* later in this lesson.

Entering What does the first sentence on the page mean? Use a translation dictionary to help you understand the words.

Beginning What do the headings on the spread say? What do you think you will learn from the text based on those headings?

Developing Underline sentences that contain the phrase *digital signals*. Ask questions you have about what these sentences mean.

Expanding Underline sentences that contain the phrase *digital signals*. Write down how these sentences help you understand the advantages.

Bridging While you are reading, create and fill out a graphic organizer on digital signals and analog signals.

LESSON 3

Make Analogies Have students compare a computer to a kitchen by answering the following questions.

- An example of computer software is a program, which has instructions for processing information. What instructions are found in a kitchen? *(a recipe)*
- Information can be transmitted to computer hardware from other places. The information is stored and processed using the instructions in programs. What is brought into a kitchen on a regular basis, stored, and processed using the instructions in recipes? *(food)*

INTERACTIVITY

GO ONLINE to access...
Technology and Communication Students explore examples of communications technology and explain their preferences. Students analyze which kind of communications technology is best for transmitting a large amount of information over a long distance.

☑ READING CHECK RST.6-8.2

Summarize Text Read aloud the second paragraph on the page, and ask students to write down examples of hardware from the reading. Ask students at the end of the reading: What are the two main purposes of hardware? Guide students to understanding that hardware is used to store and alter information.

Literacy Connection RST.6-8.1

Cite Textual Evidence Have students write down the roles of software and hardware. Review the roles, and have students correct their answers as needed. Software is the part of a computer system that consists of computer instructions. Software encodes, decodes, interprets, and manipulates data. Hardware is the physical structure where data are stored and processed.

Server Farm
Figure 2 This facility has thousands of computers that store and share the data of millions of people.

SEP Ask Questions Why do think this facility is called a server farm?

Sample: The facility tends to and takes care of data, just as a farmer takes care of his or her crops.

INTERACTIVITY

Investigate the development of communications and information transmission technologies.

Literacy Connection

Cite Textual Evidence
Underline text that supports the idea that we are in a period of exponential data growth.

Information Technologies Every day, hundreds of millions of e-mails, and billions of text messages are sent. Files are also exchanged online through "clouds" that are accessible from thousands of networks. Every year, trillions of gigabytes of information are produced on Earth, ranging from high-definition movies to printable text documents to brief messages about what to buy at the supermarket.

The software and hardware that power modern information technology (IT) depend on each other. IT hardware is the modern version of clay or stone. It serves as the physical medium where information is stored and altered. Processor chips, batteries, disks, wiring, and other components compose the physical place where software operates. In some cases, the hardware you depend on is "local," such as the processor, display, built-in memory, and other components of your mobile device or computer. Other hardware that you probably use is housed elsewhere, such as the cell phone tower that may be in or near your town, and the "farms" of servers that major telecommunications and computer companies use to store some of your information (**Figure 2**). By accessing data held on a server that is somewhere else, you can watch, listen to, read, or otherwise experience media without actually storing the data locally. We are now in a period of exponential growth of digital information production.

☑ READING CHECK Summarize Text What are some examples of hardware used in information technology?
Examples include the electronic parts that make up computers, smartphones, cell towers, and other telecommunications devices.

PROFESSIONAL DEVELOPMENT

Collaborate with Colleagues
Teachers are actively finding ways to use new technologies in the classroom. For example, some teachers allow students to use Twitter as a "back channel" to maintain a dialogue or ask questions about an activity that is happening concurrently. A second adult in the room facilitates the Twitter conversation. Meet with your colleagues, and discuss technology strategies that meet the school's guidelines or discuss current technology initiatives in order to better apply them.

Telecommunications satellites that orbit Earth can relay signals that cannot be transmitted by wires or towers. Some satellites are used to broadcast television stations and other media, and others are used by government agencies and the military.

Benefit
_____
_____

Drawback
_____
_____

Fiber optic technology is based on glass or plastic cables that transmit light at speeds around 200,000 kilometers per second. Fiber-optic cables can carry about a thousand times more information per second than standard copper cable.

Benefit
_____
_____

Drawback
_____
_____

The Internet is a complex set of interconnected networks that transmits information, largely through the World Wide Web. The Internet is usually accessed through an application called a browser, which allows people to navigate through the millions of pages. Internet connection used to require a cable plugged into a computer, but now many connections are achieved over wireless "WiFi" networks, or even mobile cellular networks.

Benefit
_____
_____

Drawback
_____
_____

93

DIFFERENTIATED INSTRUCTION

L3 Support Advanced Students
Some people still use film cameras. Have students research how film cameras and digital cameras create images and describe the advantages and disadvantages of film cameras and digital cameras.

SCAFFOLDED QUESTIONS

Use the questions below to assess students' depth of understanding of the content on this page. Have students support their responses with evidence from the text.

Cite Describe the advantages of fiber-optic cables compared to copper cables. *(They carry about a thousand times more information per second.)* **DOK 1**

Cite What is the role of a browser? *(It enables people to navigate through the millions of pages on the Internet.)* **DOK 1**

Infer What kinds of signals do cell phones, WiFi, and satellites transmit? Explain your answer. *(They transmit electromagnetic transmissions through the atmosphere since these technologies do not have wires or cables connected to them.)* **DOK 2**

 INTERACTIVITY

GO ONLINE to access...
Film Cameras and Digital Cameras Students integrate qualitative scientific and technical information to support the claim that digitized signals are a more reliable way to encode and transmit information than analog signals.

What it is Rich text and images with short-answer assessments

What it does Enables students to compare and contrast how images are captured in digital cameras versus film cameras. Students evaluate this information in order to decide which method is superior.

How to use it
• Tell students how some earlier designs for capturing photographs required 8 hours for a single exposure!

VIRTUAL LAB

Go online to access...
Virtual Lab Students will reinforce skills and practices by completing a virtual lab investigation.

LESSON 3

INVESTIGATE

Advantages of Digital Signals

HANDS-ON LAB

 GO ONLINE to download...

иInvestigate

Let the Music Play Students investigate the structure of a record and how analog signals encode and transmit sound waves. **Editable**

Class Time (30)

Group Size groups

Materials (per group) vinyl record, hand lens, microscope, poster board, tape, needle

Procedure Tips Observations will vary depending on these variables:

• how tightly the needle is secured to the cone,
• the pressure and angle of the needle to the cone
• the rate at which the record is spinning

Consider showing a video of a record player, including the sound as the record's groove rotates beneath the needle.

Focus on Mastery!

Model It! SEP Develop Models To help students think about how noise affects each kind of signal, have them...

• identify the number of possible amplitude values of the original digital signal and the analog signal. (*The digital signal only has two amplitude values. The analog signal has many amplitude values.*)

• explain how easy or difficult it is to determine what the original signal looked like before noise was added if you do not know the values of the noise. (*The digital signal only has two values, so it is easy to determine what the signal looks like without noise. The analog signal has many values, so it is difficult to determine what the signal looks like without noise.*)

HANDS-ON LAB

иInvestigate Observe the structure of a vinyl record and predict how it functions.

Advantages of Digital Signals

Although they are not continuous signals, digital signals are more reliable and efficient overall than analog signals, for several reasons.

Compatibility with Computers Computers process digital signals, and computers are everywhere—on laps and desktops, tucked in pockets, in car dashboards, and even on refrigerator doors. It's easier for computers and digital devices to do what we want them to do without having to convert analog signals first. Using digitals signals is more efficient.

Noise When an analog signal is transmitted, it can incorporate **noise**—random signals from the environment. This noise can then stay with the signal and alter the output. Static is an example of noise. Because digital signals consist of 0's and 1's, it is more difficult for noise to alter the signal, because binary code is essentially a choice between on and off. Unless noise causes a one to become a zero or vice versa, noise shouldn't affect how the digital signal is received or read.

Model It

Noise? No Problem!
The first graph shows an analog signal accompanied by noise during transmission. The second graph shows a digital signal also accompanied by noise during transmission.

SEP Develop Models
✎ Complete the models by drawing the received analog and digital signals to show how noise affects each one.

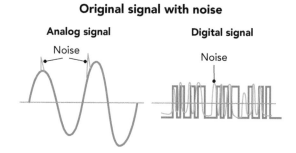

Original signal with noise

Analog signal   **Digital signal**

Noise   Noise

Received signal

Distortion caused by noise   Restored digital signal

PROFESSIONAL DEVELOPMENT

Reflect

What strategies did you use that successfully helped students synthesize the information in this lesson?

....

....

What will you do differently the next time you teach this lesson?

....

....

Analyzing Scientific Explanations

To analyze scientific explanations that you hear on the news or read in a book such as this one, you need scientific literacy. Scientific literacy means understanding scientific terms and principles well enough to ask questions, evaluate information, and make decisions. Scientific reasoning gives you a process to apply. This includes looking for bias and errors in the research, evaluating data, and identifying faulty reasoning. For example, by evaluating how a survey was conducted, you may find a serious flaw in the researchers' methods.

Evidence and Opinions

The basis for scientific explanations is empirical evidence. Empirical evidence includes the data and observations that have been collected through scientific processes. Satellite images, photos, and maps of mountains and volcanoes are all examples of empirical evidence that support a scientific explanation about Earth's tectonic plates. Scientists look for patterns when they analyze this evidence. For example, they might see a pattern that mountains and volcanoes often occur near tectonic plate boundaries.

To evaluate scientific information, you must first distinguish between evidence and opinion. In science, evidence includes objective observations and conclusions that have been repeated. Evidence may or may not support a scientific claim. An opinion is a subjective idea that is formed from evidence, but it cannot be confirmed by evidence.

Write About It
Suppose the conservation committee of a town wants to gauge residents' opinions about a proposal to stock the local ponds with fish every spring. The committee pays for a survey to appear on a web site that is popular with people who like to fish. The results of the survey show 78 people in favor of the proposal and two against it. Do you think the survey's results are valid? Explain.

Make Meaning
Explain what empirical evidence the photograph reveals.

111

Analyzing Scientific Explanations

Connect to the Real World: Global Warming Present scientific research about global warming to students. Give students an opportunity to ask questions about the research. Then have students meet in groups to evaluate the information and make a decision about how to address global warming. Have groups share their thinking with the class.

 **Write About It** WHST.6-8.1

Remind students to consider whether the people who took the survey represent an accurate proportional sample of the population of the town.

Evidence and Opinions

Teach Strategies Students may have trouble distinguishing between evidence and opinions. Give students a series of statements about scientific ideas, including some with cited sources. Base some statements on evidence and some on opinions. Have students answer these questions about each statement:

- Does the statement describe evidence or an opinion?
- If a source is cited as evidence for the statement, is the source from a reputable source or not?
- Is the statement relevant to the scientific idea?

Make Meaning RST.6-8.7

Student responses should note that empirical evidence is based on observations or measurements. Observations from the photograph include deforestation and the emission of dark smoke from the mountain.

DIFFERENTIATED INSTRUCTION

L1 Support Struggling Students: Writing
Provide frames for students to create sentences about the content on the page:

"All scientific explanations are based on _____."

"Two kinds of empirical evidence are _____ and _____."

Tools of Science

Measurement

Teach Strategies Give students a measurement in meters, a measurement in kilograms, and a measurement in seconds. Have students express each measurement using the metric prefixes *kilo-*, *centi-*, *milli-* and *nano-* and evaluate which unit is best suited for understanding the measurements they were given.

Connect to the Real World: Unit Conversions Students may mostly be familiar with the U.S. customary units rather than the SI units. Conversion equations are used by people when they need to convert quantities from one set of units to another. Have students research the conversion equations for the measurements of length, mass, and temperature. Students should then create conversion equation charts to help familiarize the class with the necessary conversion equations.

Focus on Mastery!

Make Measurements To reinforce the importance of precision, have students measure an object in centimeters. Then have them adjust their measurements to be accurate to a tenth of a centimeter (millimeter).

 Write About It WHST.6-8.2

Student explanations should include any advantages and disadvantages their chosen metric unit provides.

NEXT GENERATION SCIENCE STANDARDS

SEP.3 Planning and Carrying Out Investigations Planning and carrying out investigations in 6–8 builds on K–5 experiences and progresses to include investigations that use multiple variables and provide evidence to support explanations or solutions.

SEP.4 Analyzing and Interpreting Data Analyzing data in 6–8 builds on K–5 experiences and progresses to extending quantitative analysis to investigations, distinguishing between correlation and causation, and basic statistical techniques of data and error analysis.

SEP.3, SEP.4

Tools of Science

Measurement

Making measurements using standard units is important in all fields of science. This allows scientists to repeat and reproduce other experiments, as well as to understand the precise meaning of the results of others. Scientists use a measurement system called the International System of Units, or SI.

For each type of measurement, there is a series of units that are greater or less than each other. The unit a scientist uses depends on what is being measured. For example, a geophysicist tracking the movements of tectonic plates may use centimeters, as plates tend to move small amounts each year. Meanwhile, a marine biologist might measure the movement of migrating bluefin tuna on the scale of kilometers.

Units for length, mass, volume, and density are based on powers of ten—a meter is equal to 100 centimeters or 1000 millimeters. Units of time do not follow that pattern. There are 60 seconds in a minute, 60 minutes in an hour, and 24 hours in a day. These units are based on patterns that humans perceived in nature. Units of temperature are based on scales that are set according to observations of nature. For example, 0°C is the temperature at which pure water freezes, and 100°C is the temperature at which it boils.

 Write About It
Suppose you are planning an investigation in which you must measure the dimensions of several small mineral samples that fit in your hand. Which metric unit or units will you most likely use? Explain your answer.

Measurement	Metric units
Length or distance	meter (m), kilometer (km), centimeter (cm), millimeter (mm) 1 km = 1,000 m 1 cm = 10 mm 1 m = 100 cm
Mass	kilogram (kg), gram (g), milligram (mg) 1 kg = 1,000 g 1 g = 1,000 mg
Volume	cubic meter (m^3), cubic centimeter (cm^3) 1 m^3 = 1,000,000 cm^3
Density	kilogram per cubic meter (kg/m^3), gram per cubic centimeter (g/cm^3) 1,000 kg/m^3 = 1 g/cm^3
Temperature	degrees Celsius (°C), kelvin (K) 1°C = 273 K
Time	hour (h), minute (m), second (s)

PROFESSIONAL DEVELOPMENT

Develop Classroom Strategies

Have students design a concept wall of different types of graphs and their usages. Throughout the program as students work through topics, have students complete a graph per week related to the topic. They should vary the types of graphs they use for each topic and throughout the year. By doing this, students will become more familiar with the types of graphs and which applications each type of graph is best suited to represent.

Math Skills

Using numbers to collect and interpret data involves math skills that are essential in science. For example, you use math skills when you estimate the number of birds in an entire forest after counting the actual number of birds in ten trees.

Scientists evaluate measurements and estimates for their precision and accuracy. In science, an accurate measurement is very close to the actual value. Precise measurements are very close, or nearly equal, to each other. Reliable measurements are both accurate and precise. An imprecise value may be a sign of an error in data collection. This kind of anomalous data may be excluded to avoid skewing the data and harming the investigation.

Other math skills include performing specific calculations, such as finding the mean, or average, value in a data set. The mean can be calculated by adding up all of the values in the data set and then dividing that sum by the number of values.

Hour	Number of Ducks Observed at a Pond
1	12
2	10
3	2
4	14
5	13
6	10
7	11

SEP Use Mathematics The data table shows how many ducks were seen at a pond every hour over the course of seven hours. Is there a data point that seems anomalous? If so, cross out that data point. Then, calculate the mean number of ducks on the pond. Round the mean to the nearest whole number.

12 ducks per hour

Graphs

Graphs help scientists to interpret data by helping them to find trends or patterns in the data. A line graph displays data that show how one variable (the dependent or outcome variable) changes in response to another (the independent or test variable). The slope and shape of a graph line can reveal patterns and help scientists to make predictions. For example, line graphs can help you to spot patterns of change over time.

Scientists use bar graphs to compare data across categories or subjects that may not affect each other. The heights of the bars make it easy to compare those quantities. A circle graph, also known as a pie chart, shows the proportions of different parts of a whole.

Write About It
You and a friend record the distance you travel every 15 minutes on a one-hour bike trip. Your friend wants to display the data as a circle graph. Explain whether or not this is the best type of graph to display your data. If not, suggest another graph to use.

113

Math Skills

 Focus on Mastery!

SEP Use Mathematics Place students into small groups. Have each group discuss one anomalous piece of data. Ask students to consider the following:

- What could be the cause of the anomalous data?
- Are the anomalous data incorrect or just an exception to the case?
- Do the anomalous data merit further investigation?
- What other questions or explanations could the anomalous data generate?

Have each group explain their answers to the rest of the class.

Graphs

SCAFFOLDED QUESTIONS

Use the questions below to assess students' depth of understanding of the content on this page. Have students support their responses with evidence from the text.

Identify What type of graph would be best for comparing quantities? *(bar graph)* **DOK 1**

Identify What type of graph would be best for showing patterns of change over time? *(line graph)* **DOK 1**

Explain Explain why a circle graph is better than a bar graph to show the different types of birds in an ecosystem. *(A circle graph would show the percentage of each type of bird in the ecosystem.)* **DOK 2**

Synthesize Why would a line graph be better than a circle graph to show the relationship between predator and prey birds in an ecosystem? *(Since the predator birds would eat the prey, the numbers of the two classes would change over time.)* **DOK 3**

Write About It WHST.6-8.1

Student explanations for a different graph should include logical reasoning why their recommended type of graph is more appropriate.

DIFFERENTIATED INSTRUCTION

L1 Support Struggling Students
Provide frames for students to create sentences that elicit an understanding of the usages of different graphs.

"A _____ graph shows the parts of a whole."

"A _____ graph lets you easily compare different quantities visually."

"A line graph lets people show the _____ and _____ variables."

The Engineering Design Process

Address Misconceptions Students may hold a number of misconceptions about engineering related to a simplified view of the engineering design process. Important steps of the engineering design process are:

- identifying and researching the design problem and design task,
- imagining possible solutions and choosing the best solution,
- planning and building a prototype or model,
- testing and evaluating a prototype or model,
- communicating the solution,
- and improving a prototype or model.

The steps are iterative because engineers break down the design task into parts and jump back and forth between different steps for each part. When students begin work on an engineering task during the course, review the steps of the engineering design process.

Define the Problem

 Reflect WHST.6-8.2

Have students create a graphic organizer that shows their problem in the center, an inner circle around the problem that lists the obvious causes, and an outer circle that lists the less-obvious causes.

SEP.1, SEP.2, SEP.3, SEP.6

The Engineering Design Process

Engineers are builders and problem solvers. Chemical engineers experiment with new fuels made from algae. Civil engineers design roadways and bridges. Bioengineers develop medical devices and prosthetics. The common trait among engineers is an ability to identify problems and design solutions to solve them. Engineers use a creative process that relies on scientific methods to help guide them from a concept or idea all the way to the final product.

Define the Problem

To identify or define a problem, different questions need to be asked: *What are the effects of the problem? What are the likely causes? What other factors could be involved?* Sometimes the obvious, immediate cause of a problem may be the result of another problem that may not be immediately apparent. For example, climate change results in different weather patterns, which in turn can affect organisms that live in certain habitats. So engineers must be aware of all the possible effects of potential solutions. Engineers must also take into account how well different solutions deal with the different causes of the problem.

Reflect Write about a problem that you encountered in your life that had both immediate, obvious causes as well as less-obvious and less-immediate ones.

PROFESSIONAL DEVELOPMENT

Collaborate with the Community

Near the end of the school year, invite parents to an event in which students present and explain some of the engineering solutions they created.

As engineers consider problems and design solutions, they must identify and categorize the criteria and constraints of the project.

Criteria are the factors that must be met or accomplished by the solution. For example, a gardener who wants to protect outdoor plants from deer and rabbits may say that the criteria for the solution are "plants are no longer eaten" and "plant growth is not inhibited in any way." The gardener then knows the plants cannot simply be sealed off from the environment, because the plants will not receive sunlight and water.

The same gardener will likely have constraints on his solution, such as budget for materials and time that is available for working on the project. By setting constraints, a solution can be designed that will be successful without introducing a new set of problems. No one wants to spend $500 on materials to protect $100 worth of tomatoes and cucumbers.

Develop Possible Solutions

After the problem has been identified, and the criteria and constraints identified, an engineer will consider possible solutions. This often involves working in teams with other engineers and designers to brainstorm ideas and research materials that can be used in the design.

It's important for engineers to think creatively and explore all potential solutions. If you wanted to design a bicycle that was safer and easier to ride than a traditional bicycle, then you would want more than just one or two solutions. Having multiple ideas to choose from increases the likelihood that you will develop a solution that meets the criteria and constraints. In addition, different ideas that result from brainstorming can often lead to new and better solutions to an existing problem.

 Make Meaning
Using the example of a garden that is vulnerable to wild animals such as deer, make a list of likely constraints on an engineering solution to the problem you identified before. Determine if there are common traits among the constraints, and identify categories for them.

115

Teach with Visuals Place students into small groups. Present each group with a scenario, using an image from which they can define a problem. Have students work collaboratively to define the problem. As part of their work, students should consider the following questions in the text:

• What are the effects of the problem?
• What are the likely causes?
• What other factors could be involved?

Make Meaning WHST.6-8.1

Have students work in pairs to write down constraints. Collect the constraints into a list, and have students help you organize the list into categories.

Develop Possible Solutions

College and Career Readiness Explain that engineering requires many kinds of knowledge and that engineers work in teams with other experts, including scientists. Ask students to imagine they are part of a research team that is building a bridge that cars will drive across over a river located in a forest. Challenge students to think about the issues of building that bridge and the concerns each of the following would have:

• How would a physicist think about the problem?
• How would a biologist think about the problem?
• How would a geologist think about the problem?
• How would a mechanical engineer think about the problem?
• What kinds of information would each group have to share?

Address Misconceptions Students may perceive engineering as non-creative and have the misconception that engineers work only systematically and by themselves. However, to solve problems, engineers need to harness creativity and work collaboratively. Have students write a paragraph describing what creativity means to them. Then hold a class discussion about the role of creativity in science and engineering.

DIFFERENTIATED INSTRUCTION

L1 Support Struggling Students
Pose a problem to students related to school facilities, and guide students to define the problem using the three questions in the text.

L3 Support Advanced Students
Pose a problem to students related to local school facilities, and have students define the problem using the three questions in the text, identify and categorize criteria and constraints, and develop possible solutions.

Design a Solution

Teach Strategies Describe the following scenario to students: Two students are supposed to team together to work on a container attached to a parachute, which can be used to airdrop fragile items into areas without road access. However, the two students decide to work by themselves. Both students underestimate the complexity of the problem and try to build or design the container and parachute at the same time. One student believes planning isn't necessary and builds and tests three prototypes that she has sketched, but the prototypes don't work well. The other student keeps thinking of ways to improve his design but doesn't build any prototypes. Ask: What strategies would help this team complete their task? (*The two students should work together, break the task down into the container and parachute, and then plan, build, and test each part iteratively.*)

Test and Evaluate a Solution

📓 Make Meaning WHST.6-8.1

Students' criteria should include properties suitable for a beverage can, and constraints should include cost and availability.

Design a Solution

Engineers then develop the idea that they feel best solves the problem. Once a solution has been chosen, engineers and designers get to work building a model or prototype of the solution. A model may involve sketching on paper or using computer software to construct a model of the solution. A prototype is a working model of the solution.

Building a model or prototype helps an engineer determine whether a solution meets the criteria and stays within the constraints. During this stage of the process, engineers must often deal with new problems and make any necessary adjustments to the model or prototype.

Test and Evaluate a Solution

📓 **Make Meaning** Think about an aluminum beverage can. What would happen if the price or availability of aluminum changed so much that cans needed to be made of a new material? What would the criteria and constraints be on the development of a new can?

Whether testing a model or a prototype, engineers use scientific processes to evaluate their solutions. Multiple experiments, tests, or trials are conducted, data are evaluated, and results and analyses are communicated. New criteria or constraints may emerge as a result of testing. In most cases, a solution will require some refinement or revision, even if it has been through successful testing. Refining a solution is necessary if there are new constraints, such as less money or available materials. Additional testing may be done to ensure that a solution satisfies local, state, or federal laws or standards.

A naval architect sets up a model to test how the the hull's design responds to waves.

116

PROFESSIONAL DEVELOPMENT

Reflect

What strategies did you use to help students understand the difference in practices between science and engineering? Which strategies worked the best?

....

....

Defining the problem is an important step in the engineering design process that is often overlooked. What strategies did you use to help students successfully carry out this step?

....

....

Communicate the Solution

Engineers need to communicate the final design to the people who will manufacture the product. This may include sketches, detailed drawings, computer simulations, and written text. Engineers often provide evidence that was collected during the testing stage. This evidence may include graphs and data tables that support the decisions made for the final design.

If there is feedback about the solution, then the engineers and designers must further refine the solution. This might involve making minor adjustments to the design, or it might mean bigger modifications to the design based on new criteria or constraints. Any changes in the design will require additional testing to make sure that the changes work as intended.

Redesign and Retest the Solution

At different steps in the engineering and design process, a solution usually must be revised and retested. Many designs fail to work perfectly, even after models and prototypes are built, tested, and evaluated. Engineers must be ready to analyze new results and deal with any new problems that arise. Troubleshooting, or fixing design problems, allows engineers to adjust the design to improve on how well the solution meets the need.

SEP Communicate Information Suppose you are an engineer at an aerospace company. Your team is designing a rover to be used on a future NASA space mission. A family member doesn't understand why so much of your team's time is taken up with testing and retesting the rover design. What are three things you would tell your relative to explain why testing and retesting are so important to the engineering and design process?

- Testing helps identify unexpected design problems, which can help save time and money in the long run.

- Every time you make a change to the design, you must retest it to make sure it functions as expected and that the changes actually improve the function.

- Because most repairs will be impossible to make during the mission, it's important to test the design thoroughly.

117

Communicate the Solution

Teach Strategies Have students consider the working relationship between engineers and manufacturers. Ask: What information does an engineering team need from a manufacturer in order to produce a useful prototype? What information about the prototype does a manufacturer need from an engineering team in order to make the product?

Redesign and Retest the Solution

Spark a Discussion Explain that engineers extensively document each step of their work. Ask: In what ways can documentation help in the redesign and retesting phase of the engineering design process? Tell students to think about the prior steps in the engineering design process as they answer the question. Have students share their answers.

DIFFERENTIATED INSTRUCTION

L1 Support Struggling Students

Have students create posters that shows the steps of the engineering design process.

L3 Support Advanced Students

Have students research the story of an engineering feat and break the story down into the steps of the engineering design process.

Safety Symbols

These symbols warn of possible dangers in the laboratory and remind you to work carefully.

 Safety Goggles Wear safety goggles to protect your eyes in any activity involving chemicals, flames or heating, or glassware.

 Lab Apron Wear a laboratory apron to protect your skin and clothing from damage.

 Breakage Handle breakable materials, such as glassware, with care. Do not touch broken glassware.

 Heat-Resistant Gloves Use an oven mitt or other hand protection when handling hot materials, such as hot plates or hot glassware.

 Plastic Gloves Wear disposable plastic gloves when working with harmful chemicals and organisms. Keep your hands away from your face, and dispose of the gloves according to your teacher's instructions.

 Heating Use a clamp or tongs to pick up hot glassware. Do not touch hot objects with your bare hands.

 Flames Before you work with flames, tie back loose hair and clothing. Follow your teacher's instructions about lighting and extinguishing flames.

 No Flames When using flammable materials, make sure there are no flames, sparks, or other exposed heat sources present.

 Corrosive Chemical Avoid getting acid or other corrosive chemicals on your skin or clothing or in your eyes. Do not inhale the vapors. Wash your hands after the activity.

 Poison Do not let any poisonous chemical come into contact with your skin, and do not inhale its vapors. Wash your hands when you are finished with the activity.

 Fumes Work in a well-ventilated area when harmful vapors may be involved. Avoid inhaling vapors directly. Test an odor only when directed to do so by your teacher, and use a wafting motion to direct the vapor toward your nose.

 Sharp Object Scissors, scalpels, knives, needles, pins, and tacks can cut your skin. Always direct a sharp edge or point away from yourself and others.

 Animal Safety Treat live or preserved animals or animal parts with care to avoid harming the animals or yourself. Wash your hands when you are finished with the activity.

 Plant Safety Handle plants only as directed by your teacher. If you are allergic to certain plants, tell your teacher; do not do an activity involving those plants. Avoid touching harmful plants such as poison ivy. Wash your hands when you are finished with the activity.

 Electric Shock To avoid electric shock, never use electrical equipment around water, when the equipment is wet, or when your hands are wet. Be sure cords are untangled and cannot trip anyone. Unplug equipment not in use.

 Physical Safety When an experiment involves physical activity, avoid injuring yourself or others. Alert your teacher if there is any reason you should not participate.

 Disposal Dispose of chemicals and other laboratory materials safely. Follow the instructions from your teacher.

 Hand Washing Wash your hands thoroughly when finished with an activity. Use soap and warm water. Rinse well.

 General Safety Awareness When this symbol appears, follow the instructions provided. When you are asked to develop your own procedure in a lab, have your teacher approve your plan.

†*The atomic masses in parentheses are the mass numbers of the longest-lived isotope of elements for which a standard atomic mass cannot be defined.*

18 8A

| 2 **He** 4.0026 Helium |

13 3A	14 4A	15 5A	16 6A	17 7A	
5 **B** 10.81 Boron	6 **C** 12.011 Carbon	7 **N** 14.007 Nitrogen	8 **O** 15.999 Oxygen	9 **F** 18.998 Fluorine	10 **Ne** 20.179 Neon
13 **Al** 26.982 Aluminum	14 **Si** 28.086 Silicon	15 **P** 30.974 Phosphorus	16 **S** 32.06 Sulfur	17 **Cl** 35.453 Chlorine	18 **Ar** 39.948 Argon
31 **Ga** 69.72 Gallium	32 **Ge** 72.59 Germanium	33 **As** 74.922 Arsenic	34 **Se** 78.96 Selenium	35 **Br** 79.904 Bromine	36 **Kr** 83.80 Krypton
49 **In** 114.82 Indium	50 **Sn** 118.69 Tin	51 **Sb** 121.75 Antimony	52 **Te** 127.60 Tellurium	53 **I** 126.90 Iodine	54 **Xe** 131.30 Xenon
81 **Tl** 204.37 Thallium	82 **Pb** 207.2 Lead	83 **Bi** 208.98 Bismuth	84 **Po** (209) Polonium	85 **At** (210) Astatine	86 **Rn** (222) Radon
113 **Nh** (284) Nihonium	114 **Fl** (289) Flerovium	115 **Mc** (288) Moscovium	116 **Lv** (292) Livermorium	117 **Ts** (294) Tennessine	118 **Og** (294) Oganesson

66 **Dy** 162.50 Dysprosium	67 **Ho** 164.93 Holmium	68 **Er** 167.26 Erbium	69 **Tm** 168.93 Thulium	70 **Yb** 173.04 Ytterbium
98 **Cf** (251) Californium	99 **Es** (252) Einsteinium	100 **Fm** (257) Fermium	101 **Md** (258) Mendelevium	102 **No** (259) Nobelium

GLOSSARY

A

absorption The transfer of energy from a wave to a material that it encounters. (17)

amplitude The height of a transverse wave from the center to a crest or trough. (6)

analog signal A signal that allows for a continuous record of some kind of action. (80)

B

bandwidth The amount of information that can be transmitted in bits per second. (95)

C

concave A mirror with a surface that curves inward or a lens that is thinner at the center than at the edges. (50)

convex A mirror that curves outward or lens that is thicker in the center than at the edges. (49)

D

decibel The number of deaths per 1,000 individuals in a certain period of time. (30)

diffraction The bending or spreading of waves as they move around a barrier or pass through an opening. (17)

diffuse reflection Reflection that occurs when parallel light rays hit an uneven surface and all reflect at different angles. (48)

digital signal A signal that allows for a record of numerical values of an action at a set of continuous time intervals. (80)

Doppler effect The change in frequency of a wave as its source moves in relation to an observer. (32)

E

electrical circuit A complete, unbroken path through which electric charges can flow. (67)

electromagnetic radiation The energy transferred through space by electromagnetic waves. (5)

electromagnetic signal Information that is sent as a pattern of electromagnetic waves, such as visible light, microwaves, and radio waves. (79)

electromagnetic spectrum The complete range of electromagnetic waves placed in order of increasing frequency. (39)

electromagnetic wave A wave that can transfer electric and magnetic energy through the vacuum of space. (35)

electronic signal Information that is sent as a pattern in a controlled flow of current through a circuit. (78)

F

focal point The point at which light rays parallel to the optical axis meet, after being reflected (or refracted) by a mirror (or lens). (49)

frequency The number of complete waves that pass a given point in a certain amount of time. (8)

G

gamma rays Electromagnetic waves with the shortest wavelengths and highest frequencies. (41)

I

information technology Computer and telecommunication hardware and software that store, transmit, receive, and manipulate information. (89)

infrared rays Electromagnetic waves with shorter wavelengths and higher frequencies than microwaves. (40)

intensity The amount of energy per second carried through a unit area by a wave. (29)

interference The interaction between waves that meet. (18)

L

longitudinal wave A wave that moves the medium in a direction parallel to the direction in which the wave travels. (7)

loudness The perception of the energy of a sound. (29)

M

mechanical wave A wave that requires a medium through which to travel. (5)

medium The material through which a wave travels. (5)

microwaves Electromagnetic waves that have shorter wavelengths and higher frequencies than radio waves. (40)

N

noise Random signals from the environment that can alter the output of a signal. (94)

O

Ohm's law The law that staes that resistance in a circuit is equal to voltage divided by current. (70)

opaque A type of material that reflects or absorbs all of the light that strikes it. (45)

P

parallel circuit An electric circuit in which different parts of the circuit are on separate branches. (72)

pitch A description of how a sound is perceived as high or low. (31)

pixel A small, uniform shape that is combined with other pixels to make a larger image. (84)

R

radio waves Electromagnetic waves with the longest wavelengths and lowest frequencies. (39)

reflection The bouncing back of an object or a wave when it hits a surface through which it cannot pass. (15)

refraction The bending of waves as they enter a new medium at an angle, caused by a change in speed. (16)

resistance The measurement of how difficult it is for charges to flow through an object. (69)

resonance The increase in the amplitude of a vibration that occurs when external vibrations match an object's natural frequency. (21)

S

series circuit An electic circuit in which all parts are connected one after another along one path. (71)

software Programs that encode, decode, and interpret information. (89)

standing wave A wave that appears to stand in one place, even though it is two waves interfering as they pass through each other. (20)

T

transluscent A type of material that scatters light as it passes through. (45)

transparent A type of material that transmits light without scattering it. (45)

transverse wave A wave that moves the medium at right angles to the direction in which the wave travels. (6)

U

ultraviolet rays Electromagnetic waves with wavelengths shorter than visible light but longer than X-rays. (41)

V

visible light Electromagnetic radiation that can be seen with the unaided eye. (40)

voltage The difference in electrical potential energy per charge between two places in a circuit. (68)

W

wave A disturbance that transfers energy from place to place. (5)

wave pulse A pulse of energy that travels through an electric circuit when it is closed. (78)

wavelength The distance between two corresponding parts of a wave, such as the distance between two crests. (8)

X

X-rays Electromagnetic waves with wavelengths shorter than ultraviolet rays but longer than gamma rays. (41)

INDEX

 Page numbers for key terms in boldface type. Blue indicates Teacher's Edition entries.

INDEX

INDEX

Page numbers for key terms in boldface type. Blue indicates Teacher's Edition entries.

CREDITS

Photographs

Photo locators denoted as follows: Top (T), Center (C), Bottom (B), Left (L), Right (R), Background (Bkgd)

Covers

Front Cover: Stocktrek Images, Inc./Alamy Stock Photo
Back Cover: LHF Graphics/Shutterstock

Front Matter

iv: Clari Massimiliano/Shutterstock; vi: Paul Melling/Alamy Stock Photo; vii: Raimundas/Shutterstock; viii: Brian J. Skerry/National Geographic/Getty Images; ix: Gary Meszaros/Science Source/Getty Images.

Topic 1

x: Paul Melling/Alamy Stock Photo; 002: Losevsky Pavel/Shutterstock; 004: Mark Leary/Getty Images; 005: NOAA; 006: Wavebreak Media Ltd./123RF; 012: imageBROKER/Jim West/Newscom; 014: Brian Maudsley/Shutterstock; 017 BCL: Science Source; 017 BCR: Kenny10/Shutterstock; 017 BL: Roberto Lo Savio/Shutterstock; 017 BR: Nublee bin Shamsu Bahar/Shutterstock; 019: Denis Gladkiy/Fotolia; 021: Sergey Nivens/Fotolia; 023 CR: Graham Oliver/123RF; 023 TR: Lionel Le Jeune/Fotolia; 025: LightField Studios/Shutterstock; 026: Lipsett Photography Group/Shutterstock; 028 B: Andrey Kuzmin/Shutterstock; 028 C: Mike Flippo/Shutterstock; 028 T: Pukach/Shutterstock; 029: Goran Djukanovic/Shutterstock; 030: Mr_sailor/iStock/Getty Images Plus; 031: Vvoennyy/123RF; 034: U.S. Navy; 039: Gaspr13/Getty Images; 040 B: Arno Vlooswijk/TService/Science Source; 040 TL: Chuck Franklin/Alamy Stock Photo; 041: Anton Petrus/Fotolia; 043 B: Andrey Armyagov/123RF; 043 TR: Blend Images/Alamy Stock Photo; 045: Sirtravelalot/Shutterstock; 046: Yellow Cat/Shutterstock; 047 B: Falk/Shutterstock; 047 C: Havoc/Shutterstock; 048 B: Anne08/Shutterstock; 048 T: Tusharkoley/Shutterstock; 049 B: Yuelan/123RF; 049 T: TLF Design/Alamy Stock Photo; 050 B: Mediaphotos/iStock/Getty Images; 050 T: Science Source; 058: Amirul Syaidi/Fotolia; 059: EpicStockMedia/Shutterstock;

Topic 2

062: Raimundas/Shutterstock; 064: Smolaw/Shutterstock; 066: Room27/Shutterstock; 070: F.G.I CO., LTD./Alamy Stock Photo; 076: imageBROKER/Alamy Stock Photo; 078: Everett Collection/Shutterstock; 079 CR: Sirtravelalot/Shuttertock; 079 TL: Monkey Business Images/Shuttertock; 079 TR: Pressmaster/Shutterstock; 084: Marcio Jose Bastos Silva/Shutterstock; 089: CSP_Elly_l/AGE Fotostock; 090: Dotshock/Shutterstock; 092 BL: Tempura/Getty Images; 092 CR: Ruslan Ivantsov/Shutterstock; 092 TCR: Gallofoto/Shutterstock; 093 CR: Asharkyu/Shutterstock; 093 R: DAVID DUCROS/SCIENCE PHOTO LIBRARY/Getty Images; 097 B: Bettmann/Getty Images; 097 T: Jacob Lund/Shutterstock; 103 TL: Doug Martin/Science Source; 103 TR: Richard Megna/Fundamental Photographs;

End Matter

106 BL: EHStockphoto/Shutterstock; 106 BLC: Philippe Plailly & Elisabeth Daynes/Science Source; 106 TCL: Cyndi Monaghan/Getty Images; 106 TL: Javier Larrea/AGE Fotostock; 107: WaterFrame/Alamy Stock Photo; 108: Africa Studio/Shutterstock; 109: Jeff Rotman/Alamy Stock Photo; 110: Grant Faint/Getty Images; 111: Ross Armstrong/Alamy Stock Photo; 112: Geoz/Alamy Stock Photo; 115: Martin Shields/Alamy Stock Photo; 116: Nicola Tree/Getty Images; 117: Regan Geeseman/NASA; 119: Pearson Education Ltd.; 120: Pearson Education Ltd.; 121 BR: Pearson Education Ltd.; 121 TR: Pearson Education Ltd.

Program graphics: ArtMari/Shutterstock; BeatWalk/Shutterstock; Irmun/Shutterstock; LHF Graphics/Shutterstock; Multigon/Shutterstock; Nikolaeva/Shutterstock; silm/Shutterstock; Undrey/Shutterstock

Take Notes

Take Notes

Take Notes

Take Notes

Take Notes

Take Notes